Medical Gene

Medical Genetics

G.P. Pal
MBBS MS DSc FAMS FNASc FASc
Professor and Head, Dept. of Anatomy
Modern Dental College & Research Centre
Indore (M.P.), India

Formerly

Professor and Head, Dept. of Anatomy
MP Shah Medical College, Jamnagar, Gujarat

Formerly

Visiting Associate Professor, Dept. of Anatomy
The Medical College of Pennsylvania, Philadelphia, USA

A.I.T.B.S. Publishers, India
Medical Publishers
J-5/6, Krishan Nagar, Delhi-110 051 (India)
Phone: 22054798, 22549313, Fax: 011-22543416
E-mail: aitbs@vsnl.com & aitbs@bol.net.in

First Edition: 2009
Second Edition: 2012

ISBN: 978-81-7473-401-3

This book has been published in good faith that the material provided by author(s) is original. Every effort is made to ensure accuracy of material, but the publisher, printer and author(s) will not be responsible for any inadvertent error(s). In case of any dispute, all legal matter to be settled under Delhi jurisdiction only.

Published by:
Virender Kumar Arya
A.I.T.B.S. Publishers, India
Medical Publishers
J-5/6, Krishan Nagar, Delhi-110051 **(India)**
Phone: 22054798, 22549313
Fax: 011-22543416
E-mail: aitbs@vsnl.com & aitbs@bol.net.in
Typeset by Innovative Processors, Delhi
Printed at Sanjeev Offiset, Delhi

Dedicated to

Prof. Inderbir Singh
MBBS MS PhD FAMS

*who has been a source of
inspiration to me.*

Preface

The "genetics" is a fast developing science and is gaining an increasing importance in the medical field. This is due to the fact that more and more diseases, including many types of cancers, are now known to be genetically determined. However, most of the medical students find this subject unintelligible and hence, neglect it. This is because many available books are either dealing the subject in great detail (which is not needed by a medical student) or they fail to provide clear conceptual understanding of the subject. As a teacher, I have always felt the need of a book, which is suitable for Indian students. The aim of the book is to present a simple and concise account of the subject avoiding verbose details.

Paragraphs dealing with details, that beginners/undergraduate students can skip, are printed under the heading "Further Details" on a light gray background. Few interesting and important aspects of the subject are given in box in light colour background.

I am highly thankful to Dr. R. Badlani (Chairman, MDC&RC), Dean Prof. P.V. Wanjari and my family members for their continuous support and encouragement.

I am greatly indebted to Mr. V.K. Arya of A.I.T.B.S. Publishers, India and his entire team, for their wholehearted support, helpful suggestions and hard work which have made this endeavour a satisfying experience.

I would be thankful to teachers and students for suggestions to improve the book and also for drawing my attention towards the errors in the book.

Indore

G.P. PAL

Contents

10. Immunogenetics

11. Genetics of Cancer

12. Developmental Genetic

13. Genetic Counselling

14. Prenatal Diagnosis and Treatment of Genetic Disease

TECHNIQUES IN GENETICS

15. Some Important Techniques in Genetics

1 Introduction

- What is Genetics?
- Branches of Genetics
- Importance of Genetics in Medicine
- Classification of Genetic Disease

WHAT IS GENETICS?

It is a common observation that children of same parents resemble each other and also with their parents. It is also observed that they not only resemble in their physical appearance (facial features; height; colour of skin and hair etc.) but also in their intellect (mental powers). This is because the characters of parents are transmitted to the children through gametes (sperm and ovum). The process of transmission of characters from one generation to next (parents to children) is called the **inheritance** or **heredity**.

The next question comes to our mind is that what determines the characters in an individual. The characters are determined by **genes** which are fundamental units of inheritance. For details about genes refer Chapter 5. If one individual is short and other is tall or if one is with black hair and other with blond hair, it is all due to difference in their genes responsible for stature and colour of hair respectively. Since an individual receives genes from both parents (through sperm and ovum) hence, inherits some characters from father and some from mother. Another important fact about gene transmission is that when they are transmitted from one generation to next they don't do so randomly but follow some statistical laws (see Chapter 2). Thus the **genetics** can be defined as *the study of genes and of the statistical laws that govern the passage of genes from one generation to next.*

BRANCHES OF GENETICS

In recent past the science of genetics has made tremendous progress due to new discoveries. Human genetics can now be divided into several branches. Few important subdisciplines are as under.

1. *Cytogenetics* - It deals with the study of chromosomes (Ch. 3). Cytogenetics provides the cytological explanation of different genetic principles (Ch. 2).
2. *Molecular genetics* - It includes the study of chemical structure of gene at molecular level. This branch also includes the study of function of gene and regulation of its activity. (Ch. 4 and 5).
3. *Biochemical genetics* - Metabolic process at each stage are controlled by enzyme whose production is under control of gene. This branch deals with the **inborn errors of metabolism** (Ch. 8).
4. *Cancer genetics* - The cell cycle is under genetic control. There are many checkpoints, which control the progress of cell cycle from one stage to the next. Mutations of these checkpoints lead to various kinds of cancer (Chapter 11).
5. *Immunogenetics* - The immunological phenomenon of an individual is under control of genes. The immunogenetics deals with the genetics of production of different types of antibodies (Ch. 10).
6. *Developmental genetics* - This branch deals with the genetic control of embryonic development (Ch. 12).
7. *Behavioural genetics* - It deals with the influence of genes on the behaviour of an individual.
8. *Population genetics* - It is concern with the laws of genetics acting on human population. This branch deals with frequencies of genes in human population and the rate at which they mutate.

IMPORTANCE OF GENETICS IN MEDICINE

Maupertius (1689-1759), a French biologist, was first to observe that the conditions like **polydactyly** and **albinism** are inherited in human being. Similarly, **John Dalton** observed that **colour blindness** and **haemophilia** were inherited diseases. However, human genetics was recognised as a science only after rediscovery of Mendelism in 1900. **Garrod (1902)** discovered the inheritance pattern and metabolic nature of human disease **alkaptonuria**. In this condition, the urine of patient turns dark upon exposure to air. Patients of alkaptonuria could not metabolise **homogentisic acid** due to absence of enzyme homogentisic acid oxidase. He coined the term "**inborn error of metabolism.**" At present we know several hundred disorders which can be classified as inborn errors of metabolism. **Muller (1927)** showed that exposure to X-rays increases the mutation rate (Ch. 5). In 1959 **Lejeune** and his associates noted that the presence of an additional number 21 chromosome results in **Down's syndrome**.

In recent past more and more diseases have been recognised as genetic in nature. This is due to various new discoveries and development of modern diagnostic techniques in genetics. On other hand this may be also due to the fact that there is overall improvement in hygiene and health care. Thus because of decrease in illness due to infection and nutritional deficiency, our attention has shifted to genetic disorders. Now genetic disorders have been recognised as significant cause of disease in various age groups.

It is observed that:

- Almost about 50% of first trimester abortions are due to chromosomal abnormalities.
- Congenital malformations of genetic origin are seen in 2 to 3% of newborns. Similarly, 2% infants are born with single gene disorder or chromosomal abnormality.
- More than half of childhood blindness, deafness and mental retardation are due to genetic disorder.
- More than 5% of adult population suffers from disorders which have a genetic background. Similarly in adults many common cancers have strong genetic component (Ch. 11).

CLASSIFICATION OF GENETIC DISEASE

Different genetic mechanisms are involved in different hereditary disease. A genetic disorder may have its basis in a single gene, multiple genes or due to abnormality in chromosome itself. It may also happen that an individual who is born without any genetic disorder might acquire it during adult life due to mutation in gene or alteration in chromosome. This is common cause of malignancy in adults. Thus genetic disease may be classified as under:

1. *Single gene disorders* - This kind of disorders are due to single gene and they follow the statistical laws of Mendelian inheritance (Ch. 2). These disorders may be autosomal recessive, autosomal dominant or X-linked (Ch. 7). Thousands of disorders are now known which may be kept in this category. Some examples are given below (Table 1.1).

2. *Multifactorial disorders* - This kind of disorders are due to additive effects of multiple genes. The normal characters like height, colour of skin, intelligence, physique are determined by the interaction of many genes. Common congenital malformations like cleft lip and palate and diseases like hypertension and diabetes mellitus are multifactorial disorders. These kind of disorders are a result of interaction of gene and environmental factors.

   The multifactorial disorders follow different pattern of inheritance as compared to single gene disorders (Ch. 8).

Table 1.1

Autosomal dominant	Autosomal recessive	X-linked	
		dominant	*recessive*
Achondroplasia	Albinism	Vit. D resistant rickets	Haemophilia
Neurofibromatosis	Cystic fibrosis	Hypophospha-temia	Colour blindness
Marfan's syndrome	Sickle cell anemia		
Hypercholisterolaemia	Tay-Sachs disease		

Y-linked human trait is hairy pinna.

3. *Chromosomal abnormality* - This class includes genetic disorders which are due to increase or decrease in the normal number of chromosomes, i.e. **Trisomy 21** (Down's syndrome) or **Turner's syndrome** (XO). This class also includes disorders which results due to abnormality in the structure of chromosomes (Ch. 7). The invention of **banding** and **FISH** (fluorescent in situ hybridization) techniques has helped to detect even minor abnormalities in chromosomes (Ch. 3).

4. *Acquired somatic genetic disease* - Somatic cell divisions (mitosis) constantly occur during the life time of an individual. During each cell division there are chances that a change in the structure of a gene (gene mutation) may take place due to error in replication. It may also happen that after cell division one daughter cell may contain more or less number of chromosome (due to error in chromosome separation). These kinds of somatic mutation or chromosomal abnormalities are responsible for various cancers seen in adult life.

In the recent past, the science of genetics has made fast progress in the treatment and prevention of diseases.

SUMMARY

Heredity:

The process of transmission of characters from one generation to the next is called inheritance or heredity.

Genetics:

It is the study of genes and the statistical laws that govern the passage of genes from one generation to the next.

Branches of genetics:

- Cytogenetics
- Molecular genetics
- Biochemical genetics
- Cancer genetics
- Immunogenetics
- Developmental genetics
- Behavioural genetics
- Population genetics

Importance of genetics in medicine:

In recent past our attention has shifted from infectious diseases to genetic disorders. This is due to the fact that large number of diseases of all age groups are now known to have genetic background.

Classification of genetic disease:

- Single gene disorders
- Multi-factorial disorders
- Chromosomal abnormalities
- Acquired somatic genetic disorders.

2 Mendel's Laws of Inheritance

- Gregor Mendel
- Mendel's Experiments on Pea Plants
- Information obtained from Mendel's Experiments
- Mendel's Laws

In the last chapter it has been stated that human genetics was recognized as a science only after rediscovery of Mendelism in 1900. Gregor Mendel was first to discover the principles by which characters are transmitted from one generation to the next. He showed that the transmission of characters follows statistical laws. At present it is easy to appreciate that meiotic division determines statistical rules of inheritance. However, Mendel discovered the laws of inheritance long, before many facts about nucleus, cell division and chromosomes were known i.e.:

- Importance of nucleus in cell division was not clear.
- Chromosomes were not discovered.
- Details about cell division were not known. (It was not known that number of chromosomes reduces to half in germ cell.)
- It was also not known that hereditary factors (genes) are present in chromosomes.

Thus only after discovery of above facts in late 19th and early 20th century the mechanism of Mendel's laws of inheritance was fully understood. Clearly the findings of Mendel were much ahead of his time.

GREGOR MENDEL (1822-1884)

Mendel was born on July 22, 1822 in Austria in a poor peasant family. As a youth, he led difficult and sad life. He displayed great love for learning during his school years. His poor financial condition forced him to join Augustinian Monks in the monastery at Brunn (Czechoslovakia). This gave him an opportunity to pursue his studies without financial worries. He was sent to the University of Vienna to study mathematics and natural history. After his return to Brunn he became a science teacher in a public school. He began his famous plant breeding experiments with garden peas on a small plot of ground besides the monastery building. It took about 8 years to complete his experiments on garden peas.

Mendel reported the results of his experiments on 8th Feb., 1865 in a lecture to 40 members of Brunn Natural Science Society. Following year the report was published in the proceedings of the society. However, the significance of Mendel's work remained unattended and unappreciated up to 1900.

Why Mendel's work remained neglected for 35 years?

Following may be possible reasons.

1. Mendel's work was ignored because no one really understood it. The knowledge of statistics was necessary for proper understanding of his result. At that time no one was ready to believe inheritance to be statistical in nature.
2. Biologists were preoccupied with the Darwin's theory of evolution which appeared in 1859, just few years before publication of Mendel's report.
3. The details of cell division and importance of chromosomes were not known.

At the end of 19th century an interest in the nature of inheritance was rekindled. This was because scientists started realising the importance of inheritance in evolution and adaptation. Mendel's work was rediscovered in 1900 by three different biologists who were working independently in different parts of Europe. They were Erich von Tschermak, Hugo de Vries and Carl Correns. Their results of plant breeding experiments were similar to the work of Mendel. They came to know about the work of Mendel only after completion of their own experiments. All three biologists published their paper in 1900 and all cited the work of Mendel. Soon after the rediscovery of Mendel's work, scientific community was ready to appreciate its significance. It became clear that characters are determined by elements which we now call as genes. It was suspected that genes were probably located on chromosomes and the process of meiosis was the basis of laws of inheritance.

Gregor Mendel was elected as an Abbot in 1868. He became busy in administrative work and could not continue his scientific experiments. He died in 1884, much before his most important scientific experiments became world famous. Today he is considered as "the father of modern genetics".

MENDEL'S EXPERIMENTS ON PEA PLANTS

To find out the mechanism of transmission of characters from one generation to next Mendel carried out breeding experiments on pea plants. He selected various pea plants with contrasting characters and for each experiment he used varieties which differed in only one characteristic. Plants with the following characteristics were used for experiments (Table 2.1).

Table 2.1 *Contrasting varieties of the characters selected by Mendel.*

S.No.	Character	Variety	
1.	Height of stem	short	tall
2.	Shape of seed	round	wrinkled
3.	Colour of seed	grey	white
4.	Colour of pod	green	yellow
5.	Form of pod	inflated	constricted
6.	Position of flower	axial	terminal
7.	Cotyledon colour	yellow	green

FURTHER DETAILS

Self-pollination; Cross-pollination; Monohybrid and Dihybrid

Before going to the actual experiments of Mendel let us understand the meanings of few terms i.e. self-pollination, cross-pollination, monohybrid, dihybrid etc. When pollens of a flower fall on the stigma of the same flower then this kind of pollination is called as **self-pollination** (self-fertilization). For **cross-pollination** one has to remove the anthers from the flower before they become mature so that pollens of the same flower do not fall on its stigma. The stigma is protected against any foreign pollen by covering it with a bag. The mature pollens of the desired plant are then brought to the stigma and dusted on it with the help of a brush.

The offspring which result from cross breeding are called **hybrid**. The cross between the plants or animals differing in single pair of contrasting characters is called **monohybrid cross** e.g. cross between tall and dwarf plants (Fig. 2.1). The cross between plants or animals differing in two pairs of contrasting characters is called **dihybrid cross** e.g. plants with yellow and round seeds are crossed with plants having green and wrinkled seeds (Fig. 2.2).

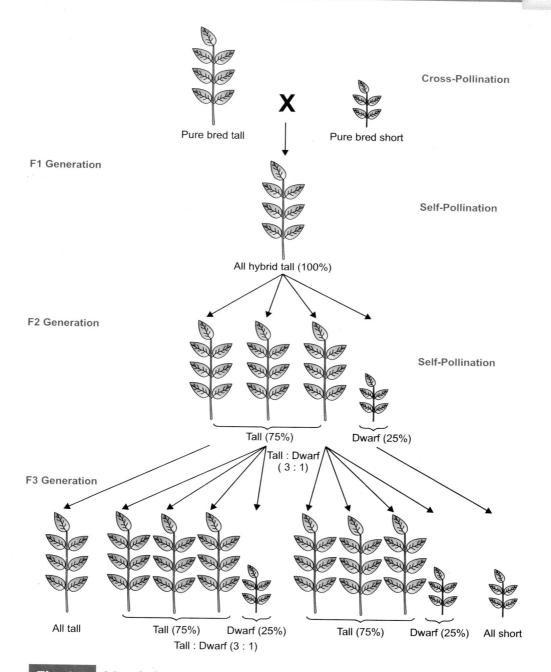

Fig. 2.1: *Monohybrid cross between tall and short pea plants.*

Monohybrid cross

Coming back to the Mendel's experiments, Mendel selected pure variety of pea plants for a single character. For example he procured pure tall and pure dwarf plants to test the inheritance of the height of stem.

1. The plants with these two contrasting characters (tallness and dwarfness) were then cross pollinated. The population (hybrid) obtained from this cross pollination was called as **first filial** generation. Mendel observed that all the offspring of first generation were tall plants (Fig. 2.1).
2. The offspring of first generation (F1) were allowed to self pollinate and thus plants of second generation (F2) were obtained. Mendel observed that:

    *   75% of offspring of F2 generation were tall and 25% were dwarf.
    *   The character of dwarfness which disappeared in first generation reappeared in second generation (F2).

3. The plants of F2 generation were self pollinated and the following results were obtained.

    i. All the offspring of dwarf plants were dwarf (Fig. 2.1).
    ii. Out of all tall plants 1/3 of tall plants only yielded tall offsprings. However, remaining 2/3 of tall plants of F2 generation yielded tall and dwarf plants in the ratio of 3 : 1 respectively (Fig. 2.1).

Mendel conducted similar experiments for all characters as noted in Table 2.1 and observed statistically similar results as observed in above experiment of tall and dwarf plants.

Dihybrid cross

Till now we have seen that Mendel carried out experiments where he crossed (mated) the plants differing in a single pair of contrasting characters i.e. tall and dwarf. However, Mendel further conducted dihybrid crosses in order to know how different pair of characters would behave in relation to each other in their inheritance from one generation to next. For this he selected two varieties of pea plants which differed in two pair of contrasting characters. For example he selected plants having yellow round seeds and crossed with plants having green wrinkled seeds (dihybrid cross). In F1 generation all plants were with yellow round seeds (Fig. 2.2). This indicated that yellow colour of seed and its round shape were dominant over green colour and wrinkled shape which were recessive in nature. When plants of F1 generation were self pollinated they produced four types of seeds in 9:3:3:1 ratio i.e. 9 yellow round, 3 yellow wrinkled; 3 green round and 1 green wrinkled (Fig. 2.2).

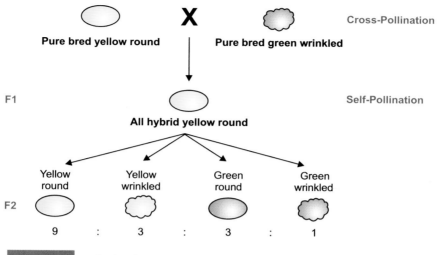

Cross-Pollination

Pure bred yellow round   Pure bred green wrinkled

F1   Self-Pollination

All hybrid yellow round

Yellow   Yellow   Green   Green
round   wrinkled   round   wrinkled

F2

9   :   3   :   3   :   1

Fig. 2.2: *Dihybrid cross between plants having yellow round and green wrinkled seeds.*

Thus two pairs of contrasting characters were transmitted independently in next generation. The F2 generation showed new combinations of characters i.e. green & round and yellow & wrinkled. Thus the roundness of seed which was associated with yellow colour in pure bred plants or in F1 generation (Fig. 2.2) was now also associated with green colour. Similarly wrinkled seed were now associated with yellow colour.

FURTHER DETAILS

INFORMATION OBTAINED FROM MENDEL'S EXPERIMENTS

What conclusions did Mendel drew from above experiments?

Following is the brief account of conclusions drawn by Mendel in later half of 19th century and an attempt is made to provide their explanation in the light of existing knowledge of present day.

1. **Each inheritable character is determined by factors. These hereditary factors were later called as genes.**
2. **These factors (genes) are transmitted from one generation to the next through gametes.**
3. **The factors for each character come in pair.**

When Mendel drew these conclusions from his experiments nothing was known about chromosomes.

Today we know that each somatic cell contains chromosomes which come in pairs. Both members of a chromosome pair are identical to each other in their morphology. Of each pair, one chromosome comes from father and other from mother. These kinds of chromosomes of a pair are called as **homologous** chromosomes. Today we also know that genes are present in chromosomes. The place on a chromosome where a gene is located is called its **locus**. Thus locus is nothing but a physical position of a gene on a chromosome. It is described in term of distance from tip of short or long arm of a chromosome. For example we may say that gene responsible for formation of a normal finger is so many micrometers away from the tip of long arm of chromosome number 10. *Thus locus may be defined as the place on chromosome occupied by a particular gene.*

But since each cell in an individual or an organism contains two homologous chromosomes, the same position (locus) on both the chromosomes of a pair contains gene responsible for same character. For example if we represent factor (gene) for tallness of pea plant as T and shortness as 't' then it may so happen that in an individual plant both the members of a homologous pair of chromosomes, at that particular loci, may have TT. Or it may so happen that one member of homologous pair may have T gene and other t. Similarly, it is also possible that both chromosomes may have tt on same loci (Fig 2.3).

Now we are in a position to understand the meaning of **Alleles**. Alleles are alternative form of a gene which is present at same locus. In other words, alleles mean a particular form of a gene. We may also defined alleles as genes occupying corresponding positions on homologous chromosomes and controlling the same characteristic (e.g. height of plant) but producing different effects (tall or short). In Fig. 2.3 genes T and t are present on same loci of homologous pair of chromosomes and are responsible for determination of same characteristics (height). Thus T and t are allelic genes. From the above description it becomes clear that Mendel was absolutely correct when he concluded that *"factors for each character come in pair"*.

At this stage let us understand two more new terms i.e. **homozygous** and **heterozygous**. Homozygous is a situation in which homologous pair of chromosomes carry the same genes (genes determining same character) e.g. **a** and **c** in Fig. 2.3. Heterozygous is a situation in which homologous pair of chromosomes carry different genes e.g. **b** in Fig 2.3.

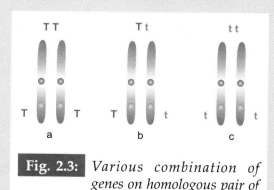

Fig. 2.3: *Various combination of genes on homologous pair of chromosomes (**a**, **b** and **c**).*

4. **At the time of formation of gametes members of the pair of genes separate from each other.**

At the time of formation of gametes the meiotic cell division takes place. The number of chromosomes reduces to half in gametes. Thus, the pair of genes present at homologous loci separates from each other so that each gamete carries only one gene, never neither nor both.

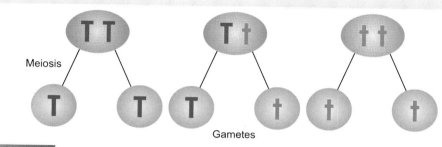

Fig. 2.4: *During gametogenesis genes present in pair separate from each other.*

5. **When plants of pure variety differing in single pair of contrasting character are crossed (mated) then only one character is expressed in first generation and both the characters are expressed in second generation.**

Let us now understand the reason why all the plants were tall in F1 generations which were obtained by crossing of pure tall with pure short plants (Fig. 2.1). Since now we know that genes for each character come in pair the genetic constitution of pure tall plants may be designated as TT and that of pure short plants as tt. At the time of formation of gametes only one member of a pair of gene will go in each gamete. When plants with these genetic constitution are crossed (mated) the offspring get 'T' gene from one parent and 't' gene from the other. All the hybrid plants of F1 generation are genetically Tt (Fig. 2.5).

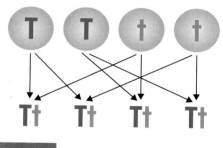

Fig. 2.5: *All the plants of F1 generation are genetically Tt. (refer Fig. 2.1 for their physical appearance)*

To determine the kind and frequencies of the various types of offspring expected we usually use squares called **Punnett squares** in genetics. The genetic constitutions of gametes of one sex are kept on top squares and those of other sex on one side. The genetic constitution of all possible zygote is then entered in squares of the grid. If we use Punnett squares for above mating we get the results as shown in Fig 2.6.

Though all the hybrid plants of F1 generation are genetically Tt but all these plants were tall similar to the pure bred tall plants with genetic constitution TT. Thus we see that though their physical appearance is same (all tall) but their genetic constitution is different (TT and Tt). To distinguish physical appearance from genetic constitution two different terms are used in genetics i.e. **genotype** and **phenotype**. The genotype is defined as the genetic constitution of an individual for any particular character or trait. The genotype of an individual is usually expressed by a symbol, e.g. tt, Tt or TT etc.

The **phenotype** is defined as the physical appearance of an individual for any particular trait. The phenotype of an individual is dependant on its genetic constitution and is usually expressed by words, e.g. "tall", "short" etc.

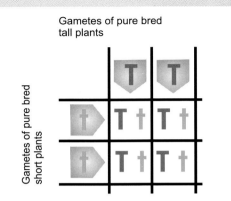

Fig. 2.6: *The Punnett's squares showing the genetic constitution of the offspring resulted due to mating between pure short and pure tall plants.*

When plants of F1 generation were allowed to self pollinate, both tall and short plants appeared in the second generation (F2).

From Fig 2.1 it is evident that all the plants of F1 generation (hybrid) were tall but in F2 generation both tall and short plants appeared. This indicates that the character of tallness dominates or conceals the character of shortness in first generation so that the character of shortness could not appear at all. From Fig 2.6 it is also evident that plants of first generation (F1) contain two different genes (alleles) of a contrasting pair of characters (Tt). Thus for expression of tallness of plant only one gene (T) is sufficient and other gene (t) remains unexpressed. Thus the character of tallness which expressed itself in heterozygous condition (Tt) in F1 generation is considered

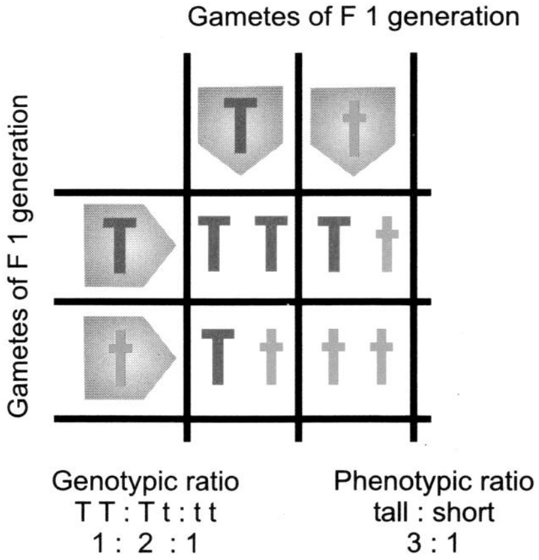

Gametes of F 1 generation

Genotypic ratio
T T : T t : t t
1 : 2 : 1

Phenotypic ratio
tall : short
3 : 1

Fig. 2.7: *When plants of F1 generation are self pollinated, we get tall and short plants in ratio of 3 : 1.*

as **dominant** character and gene 'T' is considered as dominant gene. On the other hand, the character for shortness, which could not express itself in F1 generation, is considered as **recessive** and gene 't' is considered as recessive gene. Thus a recessive gene 't' can not express itself when it is in single dose. However, the character of shortness reappeared in F2 generation where genes were in double dose (tt) and the dominant gene (T) was absent (Fig. 2.7).

6. **When characters are transmitted from one generation to next they follow statistical laws.**

When the plants of F1 generation were self pollinated both tall and short plants appeared in the ratio of 3 : 1. When the plants of F2 generation were self pollinated the tall and short plants always appeared in the fixed ratio (Fig. 2.1). In case of dihybrid cross (Fig. 2.2 the ratio between two pairs of contrasting characters, in F2 generation, was 9 : 3 : 3 : 1. An explanation of the above observation of Mendel can be given with the help of Punett squares.

   i. For **monohybrid cross** of F1 and F2 generation see Figs. 2.6 and 2.7. For F3 generation results are given in Fig. 2.8.
   ii. For dihybrid cross (as shown in Fig. 2.2) pea plants with yellow round seeds were crossed with green wrinkled seeds. If genotype of yellow round seed in **YYRR** and green wrinkled is **yyrr** then Punnett square analysis for F1 generation will be as given in Fig. 2.9.

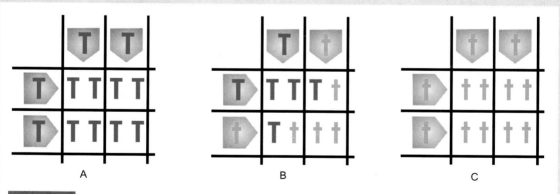

A   B   C

Fig. 2.8: *When plants of F2 generation are self pollinated, in F3 generation we get **A.** all tall, **B.** tall and short (in ratio 3 : 1), **C.** all short. Compare these Punnett squares with F3 generation of Fig. 2.1.*

7. **In case of dihybrid cross, where breeding experiments were conducted in plants showing two different contrasting pairs of characters, it was observed that assortment of genes of one pair was independent of the other pair.**

From Fig. 2.9 it is evident that each pair of contrasting characters behaves independently and bears no association with a particular character.

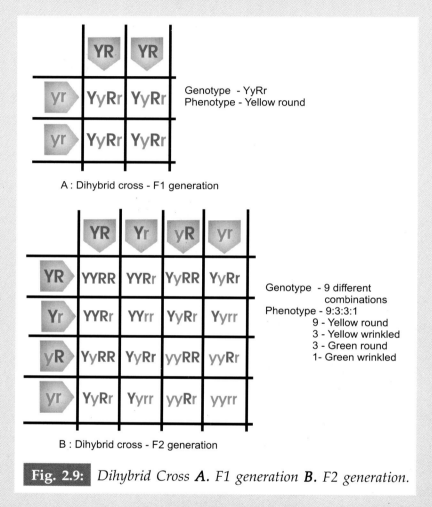

A : Dihybrid cross - F1 generation

Genotype - YyRr
Phenotype - Yellow round

Genotype - 9 different
                combinations
Phenotype - 9:3:3:1
          9 - Yellow round
          3 - Yellow wrinkled
          3 - Green round
          1- Green wrinkled

B : Dihybrid cross - F2 generation

Fig. 2.9: *Dihybrid Cross **A.** F1 generation **B.** F2 generation.*

Carl Correns who rediscovered the Mendel's work in 1900, thought that Mendel's research could be presented in the form of **"laws of inheritance"**. Following three concepts are recognized as Mendel's Laws.

MENDEL'S LAWS

In the 19th century it was thought that the traits (characters) of the parents become blended in the offspring. Mendel's experiments have shown that the factors which determine the characters (genes) do not "mix" or "contaminate each other". From Fig. 2.1 it is evident that plants were either tall or short. Plants with "intermediate" height were not observed. This observation was the basis of Mendel's first law of inheritance.

1. *The law of uniformity:*
   When plants with two contrasting characters are crossed (mated) the characters do not blend. If any character doesn't expresses in the first generation it may reappear without change in subsequent generation.
2. *The law of segregation:*
   This law states that each individual possesses two factors (genes) for a particular character. At the time of formation of gametes each member of the pair of genes separate from one another so that each gamete caries only one factor (gene). For explanation see Fig 2.4.
   When the genes of a pair are separated in formation of gametes they are completely unaltered. In Mendel's words, neither of them has *"taken over anything from the other".*
3. *The Law of independent assortment:*
   This law states that members of different gene pairs assort independently of one another at the time of gametogenesis. Because of such independent assortment of characters, new combinations of characters are produced in offspring. For explanation refer Fig. 2.9.

   In the dihybrid cross the genes for yellow-round and green-wrinkled seeds separated out independently and gave origin to four different phenotypes in F2 generation i.e., yellow-round, yellow-wrinkled, green-round and green-wrinkled. These four different phenotypes resulted from 9 different genotypes (Fig. 2.9).

SUMMARY

Mendel's observations on hybridization experiments:
- **Genes** (factors) are responsible for inheritance of character.
- The genes (factors) for each character are in pair.
- These genes are transmitted from one generation to next through gametes.
- Members of a pair of genes separate from each other at the time of gametogenesis so that each gamete carries only one gene.
- When pure bred plants differing in single pair of contrasting character are crossed then only one character (**dominant**) is expressed in first generation and both characters (dominant and **recessive**) are expressed in second generation.
- Transmission of characters follows statistical laws.

- In case of dihybrid cross the inheritance of one pair of factors is independent to other pair of factors.

Hybrid

These are offspring of cross (mating) between two genetically different organisms.

Monohybrid cross

When cross (mating) takes place between individuals or plants differing in a single pair of contrasting characters, then it are known as monohybrid cross. Such cross yields monohybrids which are heterozygous genetically.

Dihybrid cross

When cross (mating) takes place between individuals or plants differing in two pairs of contrasting characters then it is known as dihybrid cross.

Locus

The position of a gene on a chromosome is called locus.

Allele

Alternative form of a gene present at any particular locus.

Homologous

In a somatic cell chromosomes come in pairs, which are identical to each other in their morphology. These chromosomes of a pair are called homologous.

Homozygous

An individual having same allele in a homologous pair of chromosome.

Heterozygous

An individual having different alleles in a homologous pair of chromosomes.

Genotype

The genetic constitution or makeup of an individual.

Phenotype

It is physical, mental or biochemical manifestation of an individual in relation to a particular character.

Dominant

It is a trait that can express itself even in heterozygous state for a particular gene.

Recessive

It is a trait which is expressed only in homozygous state (double dose).

Mendel's laws of inheritance

- The law of uniformity.
- The law of segregation.
- The law of independent assortment.

3 Chromosomes

- Human Chromosomes
- Classification of Chromosomes
- Chromosome Analysis
- Sex Chromatin and Lyon's Hypothesis

Before the rediscovery of Mendelism in 1900 many aspects of cell division and chromosomes were already discovered. **A. Scheider** in 1873 provided first account of mitosis. **W. Flemming** in 1879, described the longitudinal splitting of chromosomes and their migration into daughter cells during cell division. In 1883, **Benden** showed that somatic cells contain diploid number of chromosomes while gametes contain haploid number. Thus when Mendelian laws of inheritance were rediscovered in 1900 the stage was set to speculate the location of factors (genes) responsible for inheritance. In 1902, **Walter S. Sutton** and **T. Boveri** proposed the **"chromosome theory of heredity"**. Sutton claimed that the newly rediscovered Mendel's hereditary factors (genes) were physically located on chromosomes. The reduction in number of chromosomes (haploid) at the time of gametogenesis and restoration of diploid number at the time of fertilization provided the explanation of Mendel's observations. Thus at the beginning of 20th century it became known that heredity is controlled by large number of factors (genes) that are located on chromosomes.

HUMAN CHROMOSOMES

Chromosomes are present in the nucleus. The nucleus of non-dividing cell (interphase nucleus) contains strands of material called **chromatin**. Chromatin is dispersed throughout nucleus and shows both coiled and extended portions. Chromatin is stained dark with the basic dyes, in regions where it is coiled and light in the regions where it is extended. The dark staining areas within the nucleus are called **heterochromatin** and light staining areas are known as **euchromatin** (Fig. 3.1). The chief chemical constituent of chromatin is deoxyribonucleic

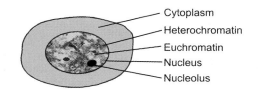

Fig. 3.1: *Nucleus showing heterochromatin and enchromatin areas.*

acid (DNA). At the time of cell division chromatin strands condense into compact structures by helical tight coiling and can be seen through the light microscope as discrete entities called **chromosomes**. Thus chromosomes are only visible as thick rod like structures during cell division (mitosis or meiosis). At the end of cell division chromosomes again uncoil to form chromatin net.

Chromosome Number

The number of chromosomes is constant for a particular species.

- The number of chromosomes in each human somatic cells is 46 which is referred as **diploid set** and designated as **2n**.
- At the time of formation of gametes (sperm or ovum) a reduction in number of chromosomes takes place. The number of chromosomes in sperm or ovum is 23 which is referred as haploid set and is designated as **n**.
- When fertilization takes place the haploid set (n) of sperm and ovum fuse to form diploid set (2n) and thus the original number of 46 chromosomes is restored in each cell of embryo.

Autosomes and Sex Chromosomes

- The 46 chromosomes in each human cell are divided into 44 **autosomes** and 2 **sex chromosomes.**
- The 44 autosomes consist of 22 pairs. The two chromosomes forming a pair are exactly of the same kind (homologous). One chromosome of each pair comes from the father and other from the mother.
- The sex chromosomes are of two different kinds, **X** and **Y**.
- The human female has 44 autosomes and two X chromosomes (44 + XX). The two sex chromosomes in females are exactly of same kind thus form a homomorphic pair.
- In human male there are 44 autosomes and one pair of morphologically dissimilar sex chromosomes, X and Y (44 + XY).

Size

Human chromosomes are only visible, with the help of a microscope, while cell is undergoing mitotic or meiotic cell division. The average size of human metaphase chromosome is around 5 mm. If we arrange the metaphase chromosomes in a row they all will measure less than half a millimeter. However, when DNA in chromosomes is extended, as during interphase, they measure few meters in length. This indicates that they become highly condensed by tight coiling during metaphase.

Shape

The shape of chromosome is different during different phases of cell cycle. As stated earlier, during interphase the chromosomes occur in the form of thin thread like stainable structures, the chromatin thread. However, at metaphase the chromosomes are thick rod shaped. Chromosomes at anaphase may be of rod, J or V shaped.

Structure

As shown in Fig. 3.2 each metaphase chromosome consists of two symmetrical halves running parallel to each other. These are called **chromatids**. Each chromosome, along their length, contains a light staining constricted area where both chromatids are attached to each other. This light staining area is called centromere. The centromere produces **primary constriction** in the chromosome. Centromere divides the chromosome into a short and a long arm that are designated as **p** and **q** respectively. Centromere is also responsible for the movement of chromosome at cell division.

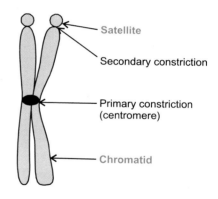

Fig. 3.2: *Structure of a typical chromosome as seen during metaphase.*

Sometimes one or both the arms of a chromosome are marked by a constriction other than the primary constriction called secondary constriction. This area is also called **nucleolar organizer region**, as it is associated with nucleolus and its formation. If secondary constriction is present in distal region of an arm of chromosome then this small fragment distal to constriction is called **satellite**.

The position of centromere (primary constriction) is different in different chromosomes but is always constant for a given chromosome. This fact is utilized in the classification of chromosomes. Beside the position of centromere two other parameters (i.e. length of chromosome and presence or absence of satellite) are used to identify chromosomes.

FURTHER DETAILS

Centromere

- The centromere is the specific and essential region of each chromosome.
- It becomes visible only after the condensation of chromosome.
- It consists of a complex of DNA and proteins.
- Human centromere consists of several hundered kilobase of repetitive DNA.
- Centromeres are the sites where spindle fibers are attached and move the chromosomes during cell division.
- There are specific DNA sequences in the centromere, which give attachment to the spindle fibers.
- In anaphase, centromere divides longitudinally, and two sister chromatids of each pair move towards opposite poles of the spindle.

Telomere

- The ends of each chromosome are made up of special DNA–protein complex called **telomere.**
- Telomere is an essential structure of each chromosome because it provides the structural stability by sealing their ends. The telomeres protect the ends of chromosomes from damage, and prevent the chromosomes from fusing into rings or binding to other DNA in the cell nucleus.
- Human telomere consists of the tandem repeats of TTAGGG-3' sequences between 3 to 20 kilo-bases in length.
- Telomeres do not contain the codes for proteins hence, they are not themselves genes.

What is telomere shortening?

When a cell divides, the DNA of chromosomes is replicated (copied) with the help of enzyme molecules. Thus the mirror images of both the two original strands of DNA are produced. However, the enzyme molecules are unable to completely duplicate the DNA strand up to the tips of the chromosomes where telomeric sequences are present. As a result, the duplicated chromosome (DNA strand) is slightly shorter than the original as it lacks the small amount of original telomere sequences. After few cell divisions the telomere sequences become too short. The loss of DNA initiate the mechanism of cell-cycle arrest and now cell is unable to divide further and may undergo apoptosis. This phenomenon leads to the aging in humans. These short telomeres are the reason why we grow old.

The phenomenon of telomere shortening is observed in somatic cells. It is not observed in germ cells, antibody producing immune cells and cells which constantly replace the gut epithelium. The shortening is not observed in these cells due to the presence of an enzyme **telomerase.** The genes producing this enzyme are inactive in somatic cells. The enzyme telomerase is responsible for duplication of DNA strand till the end of chromosome (Fig. 3.3). Sometimes telomerase even may increase the length of sequence beyond those in parent strand.

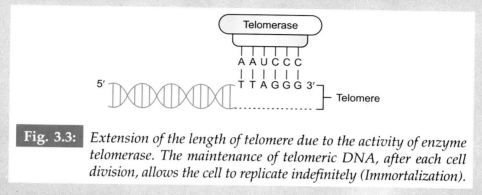

Fig. 3.3: *Extension of the length of telomere due to the activity of enzyme telomerase. The maintenance of telomeric DNA, after each cell division, allows the cell to replicate indefinitely (Immortalization).*

Telomeres and Cancer

The enzyme telomerase is absent in the somatic cell division and cell stop dividing after few divisions. However, if there occurs the mutation of gene required to prevent the production of enzyme telomerase, the telomerase becomes available in somatic cell division. This telomerase will lead to endless cell divisions because telomeres are preserved after each cell division. This may lead to the unrestricted growth of the tissue and formation of cancer. Thus the availability of telomerase enzyme may help us to stay young but has the risk of developing cancer.

CLASSIFICATION OF CHROMOSOMES

For identification of chromosomes following classifications are used.

a. *Classification based on position of centromere*

Metacentric - In this type of chromosomes the centromere is located near the center and two arms are almost equal in length.

Submetacentric - Here the centromere is slightly away from the center so that two arms are of unequal length.

Acrocentric - If the position of centromere is very close to one end so that one arm is very short and other is long.

Telocentric - These chromosomes have centromere at one end and thus have only one arm (Fig. 3.4).

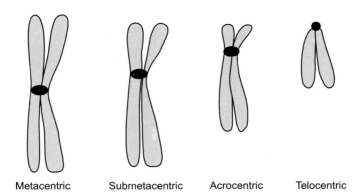

Metacentric   Submetacentric   Acrocentric   Telocentric

Fig. 3.4: *Classification of chromosome based on position of centromere.*

b. Standard classification (Denver classification)

In this classification the chromosomes are classified in seven groups as per their descending length. These groups are designated as A to G. Female sex chromosome (X) is included in group C and male chromosome (Y) in group G (Fig. 3.5).

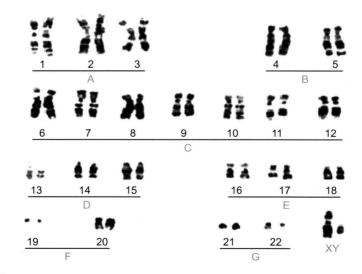

Fig. 3.5: *Classification of chromosome as per standard method. (Courtesy of Prof. Sayee Rajangam, St. John's Medical College, Bangalore)*

c. Paris nomenclature

After the invention of banding techniques (vide infra) more accurate methods for identification of chromosomes came into existence. According to this method the long and short arms of a chromosome are divided into 1, 2, and 3 regions starting from centromere. These regions are further subdivided into bands (Fig. 3.6). With the help of banding not only individual chromosome is identified accurately but also a location within the chromosome can be identified precisely. This method has helped to detect minor structural abnormalities within a chromosome.

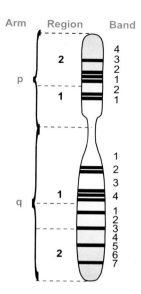

Fig. 3.6: *A chromosome showing short (p) & long (q) arms, regions & bands.*

FURTHER DETAILS

Shape and DNA content of the chromosomes during cell cycle

Most of the students are under confusion regarding the shape and structure of chromosomes. They consider that the permanent shape of the chromosomes is as shown in Figs. 3.2, 3.4 and 3.5. However, chromosomes acquire these shapes and structures only for short duration i.e., during cell division. Students should note that in a cell that is not undergoing cell division chromosomes are not visible with light microscope because they are highly extended (they are in the form of very thin threads). However, at the time of mitosis they become visible because they are now thick rod shaped. This is because thin threads of chromosomes now become highly condensed.

A cell division cycle is the process by which a cell grows, replicates its DNA and then divides to give two daughter cells. The cell cycle is divided into two phases i.e., **interphase** and **mitosis.**

Interphase is the phase of cell cycle when it is not undergoing mitosis. It is the period between two successive mitoses. It is divisible into three sub stages i.e., G1, S and G2 (Fig. 3.7).

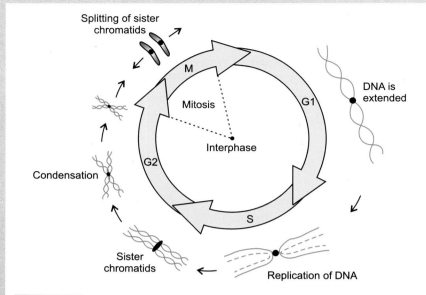

Fig. 3.7: *The cell cycle consists of four phases i.e., G1 (Gape phase or pre-synthetic phase); S (synthetic phase in which DNA replicates); G2 phase (chromosomes begins to condensed and two sister chromatids are formed) and M phase in which cell divides into two daughter cells.*

- During G1 phase chromosomes are not visible because they are thin and extended.
- During S phase the DNA of chromosomes is replicated as a preparation for mitosis. Thus the DNA contents of each chromosome become double. At the same time each chromosome also gets duplicated by the formation of sister chromatids. The sister chromatids in a pair are held together at centromere.
- In G2 phase, these duplicated chromosomes begin to condense in the preparation of cell division (mitosis).

The **M phase** or mitosis phase is the stage where cell divides into two daughter cells. Each member of a pair of sister chromatid contains single amount of DNA. Each daughter cell will get one sister chromatid from each metaphase chromosome. In the daughter cells condensed chromatids will extend and become invisible.

Only during M phase chromosomes become visible under light microscope. Thus the classification of chromosomes based on the position of centromere or on the basis of their descending length is as per their structure and shape seen only during the metaphase stage of mitosis.

CHROMOSOME ANALYSIS

The chromosome analysis is indicated in many clinical conditions for proper diagnosis of genetic diseases:

- Congenital malformations
- Mental retardation
- Repeated abortion
- Sex determination
- Prenatal diagnosis

The chromosomal constitution of an individual is called as **karyotype**. The term karyotype is also used to describe a photomicrograph of an individual's chromosomes arranged in a standard manner (Fig. 3.5). When a diagram represents karyotype then it is called as **ideogram**.

- Karyotype helps proper identification and numbering of chromosomes.
- Numerical and structural abnormalities of chromosomes can be easily identified.

Karyotyping (preparation of chromosomes)

Karyotyping is a procedure to obtain karyotype of an individual. In this procedure the metaphase chromosomes of a somatic cell are obtained and photographed. From this photograph individual chromosomes are cut and arranged according to standard classification.

For preparation of chromosomes rapidly dividing cells are used which can be obtained from following sources:

- Lymphocytes from peripheral blood
- Fibroblasts from skin
- Bone marrow cells
- Chorionic villi
- Amniotic fluid cells

Most commonly used cells are lymphocytes from peripheral blood. Following steps are involved in chromosome preparation from blood.

- Approximately 5 ml. of venous blood is collected under sterile conditions and is mixed with heparin to avoid clotting.
- The lymphocytes are separated off from red cells.
- The white cell suspension is then put in culture vial. This vial contains **culture media** and **fetal calf serum** that help to nourish the lymphocytes. The vial also contains **phytohaemagglutinin** that stimulates the cell division in lymphocytes. Antibiotics are also added to prevent infection of culture.

- The culture vial is then put in an incubator for three days at 37°C. During this incubation period lymphocytes divide rapidly.
- At the end of third day (approximately after 72 hours) **colchicin** is added to the culture vial. Colchicin has the property of preventing formation of spindles and thus arrests cell division during metaphase. At metaphase chromosomes are maximally condensed and can be easily visible.
- After two hours of addition of colchicin dividing lymphocytes are separated off with the help of centrifuge.
- These cells are treated with hypotonic saline. This causes cells to swell and chromosomes to separate.
- Cells are then fixed by adding a mixture of glacial acetic acid and methanol.
- Cells suspended in fixative are then dropped on chilled slides from a height. This helps to rupture the cell wall so that chromosomes can spread in large area. This is referred to as **metaphase spread**.

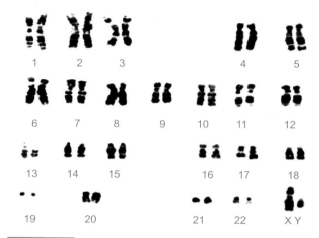

Fig. 3.8: *Karyotype of a normal male (44 + XY) (Courtesy of Prof. Sayee Rajangam, St. John's Medical College, Bangalore)*

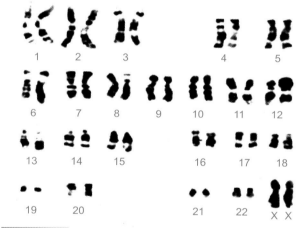

Fig. 3.9: *Karyotype of a normal female (44 + XX) (Courtesy of Prof. Sayee Rajangam, St. John's Medical College, Bangalore)*

- These slides are then stained and micro-photographed.
- From the photograph individual chromosome is cut and arranged. Thus a karyotype of an individual is obtained (Figs. 3.8 and 3.9).

Chromosome Banding

The analysis of chromosome becomes very precise with the help of banding techniques. Following staining methods are used to obtain chromosome banding.

- *G-banding:*

  In this most commonly used method chromosomes are first treated with trypsin that denatures chromosome protein. Slides are then stained with Giemsa solution that stains each chromosome showing a unique pattern of light and dark bands (Fig. 3.6).

- *Q-banding:*

  In this method chromosomes are stained with quinacrine mustard. The banding pattern is though similar to G-banding but slides have to be observed under ultraviolet fluorescent microscope.

- *R-banding:*

  If chromosomes are pre-heated before staining with Giemsa then this gives a banding pattern that is reverse of G-bandings.

- *C-banding:*

  With this method centromeric and the regions of secondary constriction are stained.

Fluorescent in situ hybridization (FISH)

This is a new diagnostic technique. It is based on the principle that a single stranded DNA probe has a unique ability to anneal with its complementary target sequence wherever located on metaphase chromosome. DNA probes are single stranded DNA sequences that have been radioactively labeled. These are used to detect the DNA fragments with similar sequences. The sites where a radioactively labeled DNA probe hybridizes with complementary DNA sequences, on a nitrocellulose filter, can be localized by autoradiography. FISH is now widely used in clinical diagnosis as results are obtained rapidly. Following type of FISH probes are used.

- *Centromeric probe:*

  The DNA sequences found in and around the centromere are repetitive in nature and specific for each chromosome. Centromeric probes are used to identify specific chromosome (Fig. 3.10).

- *Chromosome specific unique sequence probe:*

  This technique is used to identify sub-microscopic deletions and duplication.

- *Whole chromosome paint probe:*

  In this technique entire chromosome is visualized.

- *Multicolor spectral karyotyping (SKY):*

  In this technique all human chromosomes are painted (fluoresces) and a multicolor karyotype is obtained. Homologous chromosomes have similar color. This technique is used to detect deletion and translocation etc. (Fig. 3.11).

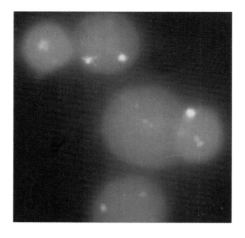

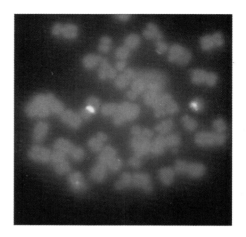

Fig. 3.10A: *FISH application to intertphase cells using X centromeric specific probe. Showing two signals in each cell thus confirms the presence of two X chromosomes.*

Fig. 3.10B: *X chromosome centromeric probe seen in two X-chromosomes of metaphase spread. (Courtsey of Prof. Sayee Rajangam, St. John's Medical College, Banglore)*

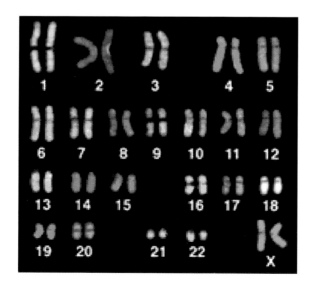

Fig. 3.11: *A spectral karyotype (SKY) of a normal female. In this type of karyotype homologous chromosomes take similar colour.*
(Courtesy of National Human Genome Research Institute, NIH, Bethesda, U.S.A.)

SEX CHROMATIN AND LYON'S HYPOTHESIS

Sex chromatin

In human being sex can be determined by observing interphase (resting) nucleus. The female interphase nucleus shows a dark stained chromatin mass attached on one side to nuclear membrane (Fig. 3.12). This is known as **sex chromatin** or **Barr body**. Barr body is observed only in females and is absent in males.

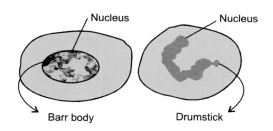

Fig. 3.12: *In human females an inactive X-chromosome is seen as Barr body or drumstick.*

Identification of sex chromatin is an easy and quick method to determine the sex. Most of the body cells in females show the presence of sex chromatin (skin, oral, vaginal or urethral epithelium and blood cells). However, buccal mucosa is most commonly used for examination of Barr body. The scrapping from cheek is taken on a slide and evenly spread. The slide is then fixed in alcohol and stained with any of the basic dyes. The slide is observed under high magnification for presence or absence of sex chromatin (Barr-body). If the cells are chromatin positive the sex is identified as female.

Similar to Barr body the nucleus of human female polymorph presents a small drumstick like structure (Fig. 3.12). This drumstick is absent in males. *The determination of sex by Barr body is not a very satisfactory method. Karyotyping determines sex accurately.*

Why Barr body or drumstick is present in females only but absent in males ?

Ohano, Kaplan and Kinosita in 1959, worked out the relationship between sex chromatin and sex chromosomes. They observed that sex chromatin is derived only from one of two X chromosomes. Out of two X chromosomes one becomes condensed and inactive; the other X-chromosome is euchromatic and active in cellular metabolism. As males have only one X-chromosome it remains active hence, Barr body is not formed.

Lyon's hypothesis

Mary F. Lyon demonstrated in 1962 that during early embryogenesis (15th or 16th day of development) one of two X chromosomes in females become condensed and inactive and form Barr body. The process of X inactivation is often referred to as **Lyonization**.

Following are the features of the Lyonization:

- Out of the two chromosomes any one becomes inactive.
- Inactivation occurs early in embryonic life (at about 5000 cell stage, 15th or 16th day of gestation).

- At the time of inactivation one X chromosome in each cell is chosen at random. In some cells maternal and in others paternal X chromosome may become inactive (Fig. 3.13).
- Once a particular X chromosome becomes inactive thereafter the same X chromosome is inactivated in all daughter cells in subsequent cell divisions (Fig. 3.13).
- Every female is therefore a kind of **mosaic** with respect to genes present on X chromosome. Because some cell have an active X chromosome of maternal origin while others have of paternal origin.
- During mitosis the inactive X chromosome is late replicating.
- The number of Barr bodies is always one less than number of X chromosomes. It means that there is one Barr body in normal female and none in normal male.

Normal Male (XY)	-	No Barr body
Normal Female (XX)	-	One Barr body
Turner Syndrome (XO)	-	No Barr body
Klinefelter Syndrome (XXY)	-	One Barr body
Triple X Syndrome (XXX)	-	Two Barr bodies

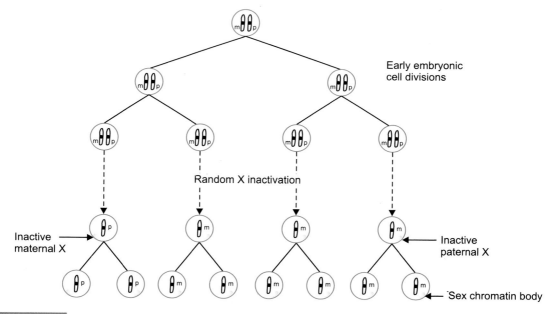

Fig. 3.13: *Schematic diagram of somatic cells of a normal female showing the inactivation of X-chromosome. Inactivation occurs around 15-16 days of gestation and is random in nature. Once a particular chromosome, maternal (m) or paternal (p) is inactivated it remains inactive in all descendant cells. Inactive sex chromosome is seen as sex chomatin body.*

Thus if a somatic cell contains more than one X chromosomes only one remains active and all others become inactive and form Barr body.

Why one X chromosome becomes inactive in females?

All female cells contain 2X chromosomes while male cells contain one X and one Y. However, the level of protein products of X chromosome is same in males and females. This is due to the fact that in females only one X-chromosome is active. If both the X chromosomes were active in each cell then the double dose of X chromosome products would have been lethal. Thus the female cells have evolved a mechanism of inactivating one of two X chromosomes. This phenomenon is called as **dosage compensation**.

Genes on Y-chromosome are not subjected to dosage compensation. Y-chromosome never forms Barr body even if there are more than one Y-chromosomes in cell. This is due to the fact that Y chromosome has very few genes that have little phenotypic effects.

History of human population and Y chromosome

As Y chromosome does not undergo recombination along most of its length during gamete formation, so the genetic markers present on Y chromosome remain together as the chromosome is transmitted from generation to generation. Therefore, the history of the human population can be traced through studies of genetic markers on the Y chromosome.

SUMMARY

- In a human somatic cell there are 46 chromosomes consisting of 22 pairs of autosomes and a pair of **sex chromosomes**. Sex chromosomes are XX in female and XY in male.
- Metaphase chromosomes are thick rod shaped. **Centromere** is a primary constriction that divides a chromosome in **short (p)** and **long (q)** arm. On the basis of position of centromere chromosomes are classified as metacentric, submetacentric, acrocentric and telocentric.
- The ends of each chromosome are made up of special DNA sequences (tandem repeats of TTAGGG-3′ sequences) called **telomeres.** Telomere provides structural stability to chromosome.
- The chromosomal constitution of an individual is called **Karyotype**.
- Chromosomes are prepared by arresting the cell division at metaphase in cell culture. With the help of special staining method chromosome show **banding pattern** that is helpful in identification of individual chromosome precisely.
- FISH is a new diagnostic technique which is used to identify specific chromosomes, micro deletion and translocation precisely.
- In females out of two X chromosomes one becomes inactive during early embryonic life and forms **Barr body**.

4 Molecular Genetics - I

- Structure of Deoxyribonucleic Acid (DNA)
- Replication of DNA
- Ribonucleic Acid (RNA)

In the last chapter we have seen that the factors (genes) which determine heritable characters of an individual, and which are transmitted from one generation to the next, are present on chromosomes. Chemically the chromosomes are composed of protein and nucleic acid. However, only the nucleic acid is responsible for inheritance. There are two types of nucleic acids:

1. Deoxyribonucleic acid - DNA
2. Ribonucleic acid - RNA

DNA is mainly found in chromosomes but is also found in mitochondria. RNA is mainly found in nucleolus within the nucleus. The other sites where RNA is found are ribosome and cytoplasm. Genes are made up of DNA. Hence, the chemical structure of DNA will help us to understand the function of genes.

STRUCTURE OF DNA

1. *Chemical composition of DNA:*
   DNA is composed of three different types of chemical compounds.
   - *Sugar molecule* - It is called deoxyribose, which is a pentose sugar (Fig. 4.1).
   - *Phosphoric acid* (Fig. 4.2).

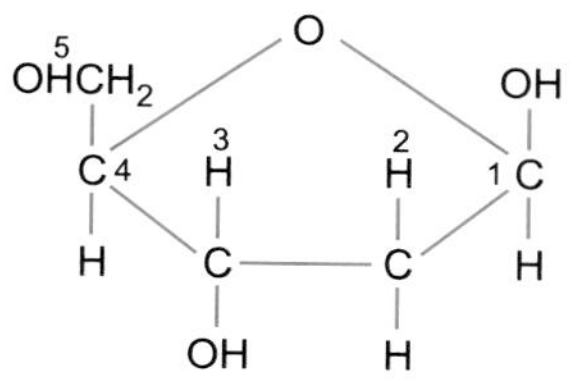

Fig. 4.1: *A molecule of deoxyribose.*

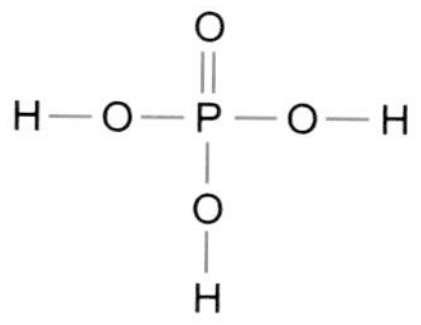

Fig. 4.2: *Phosphoric acid.*

* *Nitrogenous bases* (Fig. 4.3).

These are of four types

>   Adenine - (A)
>   Thymine - (T)
>   Cytosine - (C)
>   Guanine - (G)

Adenine and guanine are classified as purines while cytosine and thymine as pyramidines.

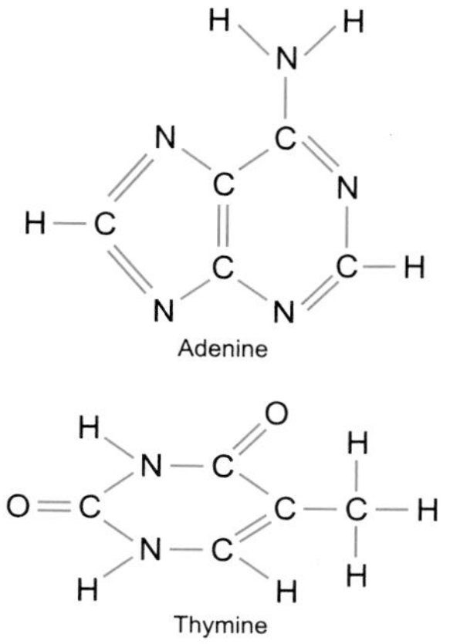

2. *Molecular structure of DNA:*
   * DNA is in the form of long chained polymer which inturn is formed by linkage of nucleotide molecules.
   * Each nucleotide molecule is formed of one molecule of deoxyribose, one molecule of

Fig. 4.3: *A molecule of adenine and thymine.*

   phosphoric acid and one nitrogenous base. As there are four nitrogenous bases there are four types of nucleotide.
   * In a nucleotide the phosphate molecule is attached to fifth carbon atom of the sugar (deoxyribose) and the nitrogenous base is attached to first carbon atom (Fig. 4.4).

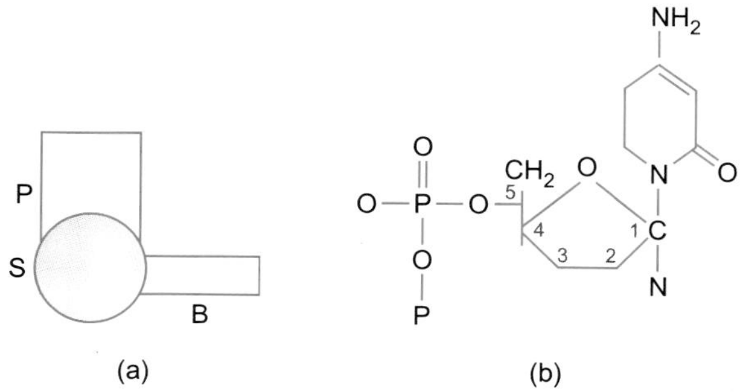

(a)   (b)

Fig. 4.4: *a. Schematic diagram of a molecule of nucleotide (P=phosphoric acid , S=sugar and B=nitrogenous base) b. Chemical structure of a molecule of nucleotide.*

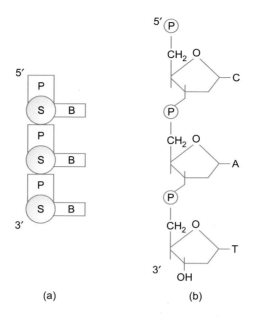

(a)   (b)

Fig. 4.5: *A polynucleotide chain; **a**. Schematic diagram, **b**. Structural diagram (C=cytosine, A=adenine and T=thymine).*

- The phosphate molecule of a nucleotide is joined to the third carbon atom of the deoxyribose of the next nucleotide. Thus the sugar and phosphate molecules are arranged in a linear fashion to form a polynucleotide chain. The nitrogenous base is attached to sugar molecule and is directed at right angle to the long axis of polynucleotide chain (Fig. 4.5).
- Each polynucleotide chain has marked ends. In Fig. 4.5 at the upper end the 5th carbon atom of sugar molecule is not linked to other nucleotide and terminate in phosphate. This end is called as 5′ or 5′ P terminus. The other end of chain ends in sugar molecule whose 3rd carbon atom is not linked to other nucleotide and bear 3′-OH group (hydroxyl group). This end of polynucleotide chain is called 3′ end or 3′ OH terminus.
- According to Watson and Crick (1953) the DNA molecule is made up of two such polynucleotide chains which lie side by side but run in opposite directions (antiparallel). One chain runs in 5′-3′ direction, the other in 3′-5′ direction (Fig. 4.6).
- Sometimes the 3′ end is called "head" end and 5′ end as "tail" end of DNA strand.
- The two chains are held together by hydrogen bonds between nitrogenous bases (Fig. 4.6).
- The pairing between nitrogenous bases is fixed i.e. adenine (A) always pairs with thymine (T) and cytosine (C) with guanine (G). The specific pairing is due to the fact that their molecules are complementary and perfect hydrogen bonds are

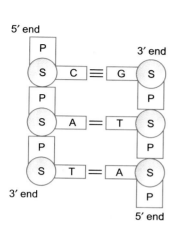

(a)

(b)

Fig. 4.6: *Antiparallel polynucleotide chains showing sugar-phosphate backbone and nitrogenous base pairing. The nitrogenous base C always pairs with G (guanine) while A with T. **a.** Schematic diagram, **b.** Structural diagram.*

formed easily. A and T share two hydrogen atoms while C and G are joined by three hydrogen bonds.

- As there is specific base pairing two strands of DNA are complementary to each other. If the sequence of bases on one chain is A T G C A then the corresponding region on other chain will have the sequence T A C G T.

- Two complementary chains (polynucleotides chains) of DNA are twisted around each other to form what is called **double helix**. One turn of helix measures about 3.4 nm and contains 10 paires of nucleotides. The distance between two adjacent nucleotides is 0.34 nm. The diameter of helix is about 2 nm (Fig. 4.7).

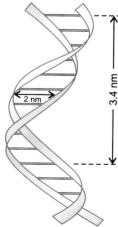

Fig. 4.7: *The DNA double helix, one turn of helix measures about 3.4 nm and contains 10 pairs of nucleotides.*

How DNA helix is packed in a chromosome ?

Each chromosome is composed of a double helix of DNA. The length of DNA filament of a single chromosome measures up to 50 mm. but the chromosome is only 5 m in length. Thus there is about 10,000 times reduction in length. This is due to the fact that in a metaphase chromosome filament of DNA undergoes several orders of coiling (Fig. 4.8).

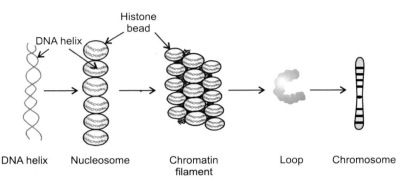

Histone bead

DNA helix

DNA helix   Nucleosome   Chromatin   Loop   Chromosome
filament

Fig. 4.8: *Solenoid model of DNA coiling.*

- The first order of coiling is due to the coiling of DNA double helix itself.
- The filaments of DNA double helix form coils around histone complex (histone beads). The structure formed by secondary coiling of DNA filaments around histone beads is called **nucleosome**. The DNA filaments wound twice around each histone bead and contains around 146 nucleotide pairs. Nucleosomes are attached to one another forming long chain.
- The chain of nucleosome coils on itself in a helical manner to form **chromatin filament**.
- Chromatin filament forms loops.
- The loops further coil on themselves to form a chromosome which is visible under light microscope during metaphase stage of cell division.
  The above description of coiling is the **solenoid model** of chromosome structure.

AMAZING PACKING OF DNA

The straightened strand of DNA, taken from a typical human chromosome, measures about 5 cm in length. It may have about half a billion to 3 billion nucleotides. If we arrange the DNA of all the 46 human chromosomes end to end, they would measure 2 meters or 6 ft. in length. Human body consists of approximately 10^{14} cells and if all the DNA of an individual is joined end to end the total length of DNA will be 2×10^{14} m or 2×10^{11} km. This length is too much and equal to reach from earth to sun and back about 500 times.

Mitochondrial DNA

- Besides nuclear DNA mitochondria also contain DNA.
- Mitochondrial DNA, similar to the nuclear DNA, is also double–stranded but arranged in circle.
- It consists of 16.6 kb nucleotide base pairs.
- Mitochondrial DNA codes for 37 genes (22 genes for tRNAs, 2 for rRNA and 13 genes for enzymes responsible for oxidative phosphorylation, OXPHOS). These enzymes are involved in energy production. Therefore the mitochondrial abnormalities are associated with the loss of coupling between oxidation and phosphorylation. The mitochondrial disorders (due to mutation in mtDNA) are extremely variable because of *hetroplasmy* (see Chapter 7). Characteristics and examples of mitochondrial disorders are given in Chapter 8.
- There is very little repetitive DNA (extragenic DNA) in the mitochondria.
- At the time of fertilization, mitochondria of sperm are not transmitted to oocyte. The zygote contains mitochondria derived exclusively from mother (oocyte). Thus mitochondrial DNA abnormality follows the maternal pattern of inheritance (disorder affects both males and females but transmitted only through females—see Chapter 7).

MITOCHONDRIAL DNA ACTS AS MARKER TO TRACE THE HUMAN ANCESTRY

The mitochondrial DNA does not undergo genetic recombination. This resembles somewhat to the Y-chromosome (page 33, Chapter 3). Hence, mtDNA acts as good genetic marker for tracing human ancestry. Another fact is that human mtDNA evolves changes in sequence at an approximately constant rate (1 change per mitochondria lineage every 3800 years). With the help of mtDNA we could know that modern human population originated in Sub-Saharan Africa approximately 130,000 years ago. From here it started migrating to the various parts of the world. They first migrated out of Africa to the Middle-East about 100,000 years ago. From there they migrated to the east and south Asia (67,000 years ago), to Australia and to Europe about 40,000 years ago. From East Asia migration took place to North America (about 20,000 years back) and from there to South America about 13,000 years ago.

REPLICATION OF DNA

Chromosomes duplicate themselves during cell division as at the end of mitosis the two daughter cells contain all the 46 chromosomes, which were present in parent cell. The duplication of chromosome means duplication of DNA. The double helix model of Watson & Crick has provided a very simple mechanism of DNA replication.

- During S (synthesis) phase of cell division (see Ch. 11) the tightly coiled DNA filament gets uncoiled. The two strands of DNA molecules separate through the action of enzymes. This is achieved due to breakage of hydrogen bonds between nitrogenous bases. Two polynucleotide chains thus separated are complimentary to one another (Fig. 4.9a).
- The position along a DNA strand at which replication begins is called **replication origin.** From the site of origin replication begin in both the directions. Due to this bubble shaped structures are formed called replication bubbles.
- The region at which parental strands are separating and new strands are being synthesized is called **replication fork.** Thus from origin two replication forks move in opposite directions.
- The process of DNA replication starts at multiple points in the DNA double helix (Fig. 4.9b).

This helps to reduce the total replication time. These replication origin sites are placed about 40,000 nucleotide pairs apart. Thus each chromosome replicates by many thousands origin sites.

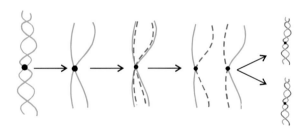

Fig. 4.9a *The process of replication.*

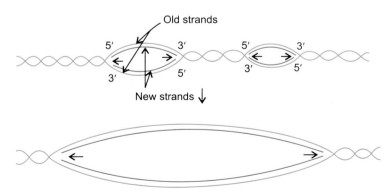

Old strands

5′　　　3′　　　5′　　　3′

3′　　　5′　　　3′　　　5′

New strands ↓

Fig. 4.9b *Schematic drawing showing multiple points of origin of replication. Replication is bidirectional and replication bubles fuse where they meet.*

At each replication fork about 10 to 100 nucleotide pairs are added per second. A chromosome usually takes 15 to 30 minutes to replicate. Because all the chromosomes of a cell do not replicate simultaneously, complete replication of all chromosomes of a cell takes 8 to 10 hours.

- Each nucleotide of old chain, because of specific base pairing, attracts its complementary nucleotide from the cytoplasm of cell.
- The new nucleotides attach with their complementary nucleotides on the old chain with the help of hydrogen bonds (Fig. 4.9b).

Nucleotides are added one at a time to the growing end of a DNA strand.

- The sugar radicals of neighbouring nucleotides are then attached to each other through their phosphate components. Thus a new polynucleotide chain is formed opposite to old polynucleotide chain. Each of the new strands is elongated only at the 3'end.
- The two daughter polynucleotide chains are exactly identical to the original parent chain. The significance of this is that *the genetic information is conserved and transmitted to each daughter cell.*
- The method of DNA replication is described as **semiconservative** as only one strand of DNA double helix is newly synthesized while other strands is of parental origin (Fig. 4.9).

What are Okazaki fragments?

At the Y shaped replicating fork, the synthesis of new DNA strands occurs in 5' to 3' direction. One strand is synthesized as a continuous strand and is called **leading**

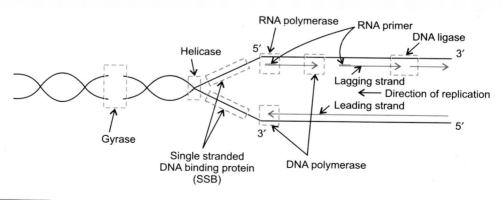

Fig. 4.10: *A detailed diagram of DNA replication at the replication fork. The synthesis in the leading strand is continuous while in lagging strand is discontinuous. Lagging strands (Okazaki fragments) later joins with each other with the help of enzyme ligase. Diagram shows various enzymes involved in replication.*

strand. The other strand is synthesized in pieces hence, called **lagging strand** (Fig. 4.10). The pieces of lagging strand are called **Okazaki fragments**. Later these fragments are joined together by the enzyme DNA **ligase** to form a continuous strand.

Why DNA strand is synthesized in fragments on lagging strand?

The synthesis of new DNA strand occurs in 5′ to 3′ direction only. The unwinding of double helix provides only a small region of parental strand in the lagging strand on which first a RNA primer is synthesized and then DNA strand is added in 5′ to 3′ direction. The DNA synthesis continues till the RNA primer of the previous fragment is reached. The RNA primer of previous fragment is now removed and DNAs of these two adjacent fragments now join with the help of DNA ligase (Fig. 4.10).

FURTHER DETAILS

Role of enzymes in replication

- The unwinding of the double helix to separate the parental strand is due to enzyme **helicase (Fig. 4.10).**
- After separation the single strand is stabilized to act as template for DNA synthesis. (*Without stabilization strands of double helix will again try to come together.*) This is achieved by **single stranded DNA binding protein**.
- It is necessary that for replication each DNA strand should be straight. Hence, separation of two strands is not enough, they should also get rid off their helical turns (torsional stress). This is achieved by enzyme **gyrase.** The DNA gyrase induces a double strand break ahead of the replication fork to relieve of torsion stress by making full rotation to unwind each of the turn. Once the torsion stress is relieved the broken strands of DNA rejoin under the influence of gyrase.
- The first few nucleotides are synthesized to serve as primer for elongation of new daughter strand. The RNA primer is formed with the help of enzyme **RNA polymerase.** The primer may consist up to 12 nucleotides of RNA. This primer is later removed.
- On the RNA primer now new DNA strand is added with the help of **DNA polymerase.**
- The DNA polymerase forms the sugar-phosphate bond between adjacent nucleotides in new chain. It also recognizes the appropriate nucleotide to incorporate in new chain.

RIBONUCLEIC ACID (RNA)

RNA is present in the nucleolus and cytoplasm. In human being RNA is not concerned with inheritance. It is synthesized from DNA template (model).

Following are the differences between DNA and RNA.

S.No.	DNA	RNA
1.	DNA is present in chromosomes.	RNA is present in nucleolus and cytoplasm.
2.	The sugar molecule in DNA is deoxyribose.	The sugar molecule in RNA is ribose.
3.	DNA is double stranded helical structure formed by nucleotides arranged in a linear sequence.	RNA is a single stranded which is formed by nucleotides arranged in a linear sequence.
4.	Four nitrogenous bases are found in DNA (A, T, C and G).	It also contains 4 bases but thymine is replaced by uracil (A, U, C and G).
5.	DNA is the hereditary material and information for life process are encoded in DNA molecules.	It is nonhereditary in nature and helps in protein synthesis.

There are three types of RNAs:

1. Messenger RNA (mRNA)
2. Ribosomal RNA (rRNA)
3. Transfer RNA (tRNA)

Messenger RNA (mRNA)

Messenger RNA is synthesized inside the nucleus. It is formed as a complementary chain to the DNA strand by the process of transcription. Thus it carries all the genetic information present on DNA strand in the form of sequence of base arrangements. However, the thymine of DNA is substituted by uracil of mRNA. Messenger RNA molecules are composed of several hundred to several thousand nucleotides arranged in a single strand. After formation of mRNA in nucleus it comes out through nuclear pores into the cytoplasm where it gets attached to ribosomes. The genetic information on mRNA (the sequence of base arrangement) is used for protein synthesis. The life span of mRNA varies from few hours to few days. The mRNA constitutes about 10% of the total RNA present in a cell.

Ribosomal RNA (rRNA)

The rRNA occurs in ribosomes and constitute about 80% of the total RNA present in the cell. It is synthesized inside the nucleus. The part of the DNA which codes for rRNA is associated with nucleolus and is called nucleolar organizer. This region of nucleolus contains DNA loops of chromosomes 13, 14, 15, 21 and 22 which contains genes for ribosomal RNA, RNA polymerase and transcription factors. Within the nucleolus ribosomal RNA are synthesized and organized into small and large ribosomal subunits, which migrate to the cytoplasm through the nuclear pores.

The ribosome is made up of two subunits i.e. large and small. The rRNA occurs in the form of particles of three different dimensions i.e. 28s, 18s and 5s. The large subunit of ribosome contains 28s and 5s molecules whereas 18s molecules are present in small subunit of ribosome.

Ribosomal RNA helps in the synthesis of protein.

Transfer RNA (tRNA)

A tRNA molecule is a single stranded and consists of about 75 to 80 nucleotides. It is synthesized at particular region of DNA. The polynucleotide chain is bent in middle and forms two arms on sides. This kind of shape of tRNA is called as "**clover leaf model**". The tRNA plays main role in protein synthesis. It gets attached to specific amino acid in cytoplasm. As there are 20 amino acids there are many tRNA. After the attachment of amino acid to tRNA it is transported to the ribosome for protein synthesis. There are four different special sites in the molecule of tRNA (Fig. 4.11).

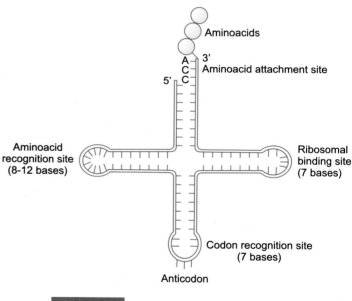

Fig. 4.11: *Clover leaf model of tRNA.*

- *Recognition site* - It contains specific base sequence which can recognise correct amino acid.
- *Amino acid attachment site* - The specific amino acid gets attached to this site.
- *Codon recognition site* - This site has 3 bases whose sequence is complementary with a codon in mRNA.
- *Ribosomal recognition site* - This helps tRNA to recognise the ribosome for attachment.

SUMMARY

DNA

- Genes are composed of DNA molecules and are responsible for inheritance of characters. They are present in nucleus and mitochondria.
- DNA is in the form of long chain which inturn is formed by fusion of nucleotide molecules. (A nucleotide molecule itself is formed of one molecule of deoxyribose sugar, one molecule of phosphate and one nitrogenous base.)
- The DNA molecule is made up of two polynucleotide chains which lie side by side but runs in opposite directions (antiparallel).
- There are rigid pairing between bases on two parallel running DNA strands.
- The double helix of DNA is tightly coiled within the chromosome.
- At the time of cell division chromosomes duplicate themselves by the process of replication.
- In the process of replication a new strand of DNA is synthesized against the parent strand.
- Many enzymes play important role in the replication i.e., helicase, single stranded DNA binding protein, gyrase, RNA polymerase and DNA polymerase.

RNA

- RNA is not responsible for inheritance.
- RNA is present in nucleolus and cytoplasm.
- The sugar molecule in RNA is ribose and nitrogenous bases are A, G, C and U.
- There are three different types of RNAs (mRNA, rRNA and tRNA) which play an important role in synthesis of protein.

5 Molecular Genetics - II

- Genes
- Genetic Code
- Transcription
- Translation
- Regulation of Gene Expression
- Mutation

GENES

Genes are situated in the chromosomes and are responsible for the determination of inheritable characters. It is estimated that there are about 30,000 genes located on 23 human chromosomes (as per Human Genome Project, 2001). Genes are arranged in a single linear order in the chromosome similar to arrangement of beads on a string. There exists two different kinds of genes in chromosomes i.e. **structural genes** and **control genes (regulatory genes)**. Function of structural genes is to synthesize specific proteins, while control genes regulate the activity of structural genes. The function of regulatory genes is to either promote or inhibit the sequences of events by which a structural gene is translated into a product.

Molecular Structure of a Gene

Chemically gene is composed of DNA. In simple language the structural gene can be defined as *"a segment of DNA which contains the information (code) for synthesis of one complete polypeptide chain (or an enzyme)."* Thus genes are nothing but instructions for making proteins.

As polypeptide chain is made of sequential arrangement of specific amino acids, it was expected that there must be a contiguous sequence of DNA coding for these amino acids in a structural gene. But now it is known that there are many non-coding sequences which are called "**introns**", interposed between the coding sequences "**exons**". The number of introns in various genes is variable and sometimes it may so happen that introns are much larger than exons (coding sequences). Though introns are transcribed (vide infra) but are not included in mature mRNA.

The structure of a structural gene not only contains the sequences of exon and introns but also possesses **flanking regions** at the ends. These flanking regions are important for regulation of gene (Fig. 5.1).

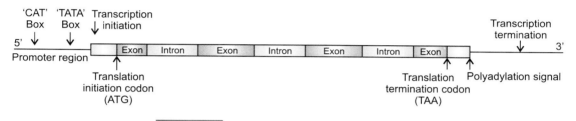

Fig. 5.1: *Structure of a structural gene*

At 5′ end the flanking region is made up of DNA sequences which controls transcription. This region is called as promoter region and contains "TATA" box and "CAT" box. The TATA box consists of GGGCGGG sequences and CAT box CCAAT. The presence of TATA and CAT box is essential for transcription because the regulation of transcription is affected through the binding of transcription factors to this region. Soon after promoter region there is code for initiation of transcription which is followed by the code for initiation of translation (ATG). At 3′ end the flanking region consists of translation termination codon (TAA), which is followed by poly (A) cap codon (refer transcription).

FURTHER DETAILS

DNA Sequences

The DNA is present in nucleus and in mitochondria. Out of total DNA content of the chromosomes only a small proportion act as genes. There are only about 30,000 genes in human. The rest of vast amount of DNA sequences are transcriptionally inactive. They do not act as genes and hence, known as **junk DNA.** The junk DNA consists of repetitive DNA sequences. The DNA present in the nucleus, therefore can be grouped into two category i.e., **genic DNA** and **extragenic DNA.**

The genic DNA consists single or low copy number DNA sequences while extragenic DNA consists of highly repetitive DNA sequences.

A – Genic DNA

Some facts about genes are as under:

- Most of the genes in the chromosome are usually present below telomere.
- Distribution of genes in different chromosomes also varies i.e., chromosome number 19 and 22 are gene rich while chromosome number 4 and 18 contain very few genes.
- Some genes are small (consisting of single exon) and others are very large (consisting up to 79 exons). A single exon may contain many nucleotide base pairs.
- There are about 30,000 genes in human genome.
- Most of human genes are single (single-copy genes). Genes coding for enzymes hormones, receptors and structural and regulatory protein are single-copy genes.
- Beside single copy genes there are many genes which have similar function i.e., more than one gene for same function. For example many α-globin genes are present on chromosome number 16 and many β-globin genes are present in groups on chromosome number 11. Similarly, many copies of genes coding for the ribosomal RNAs are present on the short arm of various acrocentric chromosome. Theses genes are known as **multigene families** and may arise through gene duplication.

B – Extragenic DNA

A large number of DNA sequences are made up of repetitive DNA sequences that are not transcribed (non-genic or extragenic). Though these DNA sequences are known as junk DNA but some portion of lit may play a role in the regulation of gene expression. The repetitive DNA sequence are of two different types i.e., **tandemly repeated DNA sequences** and **interspersed repetitive DNA sequences.**

Tandemly Repeated Sequences

- The tandemly repeated DNA sequences consists of tandem repeat of DNA sequences which are non-coding.
- These are classified as **satellite DNA, minisatellite DNA** and **microsatellite DNA.**
- The satellite DNA consists of short tandemly repeated DNA sequences and is present near centromere.
- **The minisatellite** DNA mainly consists of telomeric DNA. Human telomere consists of the tandem repeats of TTAGGG sequences between 3 to 20 kilo-bases in length. The telomere protects the ends of chromosomes (refer Chapter 3).
- Beside telomeric DNA microsatellite are also present at other location in the chromosomes. These minisatellite consists of highly variable DNA sequences (also called hypervariable minisatellite DNA). The hypervariability of these tandem repeats of sequences forms the basis of **DNA finger printing.**

- The microsatellite DNA are tandem repeats of few (one to four) base pair sequences. These repeat base pair sequences are present throughout the genome.

Interspersed Repeated Sequences

Some repetitive DNA sequences are interspersed throughout the genome. They are either short interspersed nuclear elements (DNA sequences of approximately 300 bp) orlong interspersed nuclear elements (DNA sequences of up to 6000 bp).

What are the functions of Extragenic DNA?

At present we do not know about the function of vast amount of repetitive DNA sequences in the genome. Though the extragenic DNA is considered as Junk DNA but some functional role may be attributed to it.

Some portion of it plays a role in gene expression. The hypervariability of minisatellite DNA forms the basis of finger printing.

The telomeric minisatellite DNA plays a role in the stability of chromosomes.

GENETIC CODE

- The function of a gene is to direct the synthesis of protein.
- Protein is made up of polypeptide chains which inturn are made up of amino acids. The amino acids are linked together in a particular sequence in a polypeptide chain.
- The numbers, types and arrangement of amino acids in a protein molecule determines the structure and function of that protein.
- There are only 20 different amino acids in proteins.
- A sequence of three bases on DNA strand codes for one amino acid. There are four different types of nitrogenous bases in DNA (A, C, T and G). Their linear arrangement on DNA strand determines the sequence of amino acids in a protein molecule.
- As there are only 4 nitrogenous bases, and if a single base codes for one amino acid then we shall get codes for only 4 amino acids ($4 \times 1 = 4$). If two bases code for one amino acid then we get codes for only 16 amino acids ($4^2 = 16$). It is not enough for coding all amino acids. However, if 3 bases code for one amino acid then we get codes for large numbers ($4^3 = 64$). Thus genetic information (code) is stored within the gene (DNA molecule) in the form of a sequence of three bases determining one amino acid. This is called as **triplet code**. Table 5.1 contains the names of 20 amino acids and their DNA codes.
- By the process of "transcription" (vide infra) these triplet codes are transferred from DNA to mRNA. The triplet of nucleotide bases in mRNA which code for a particular amino acid is called **codon**.

Table 5.1 *Names of amino acids, their DNA codes and mRNA codons.*

S.No.	Name of Amino acid	DNA codes	RNA codons
1.	Alanine	CGA, CGG	GCU, GCC
2.	Arginine	GCA, GCG	CGU, CGC
3.	Asparagine	TTA, TTG	AAU, AAC
4.	Aspartic acid	CTA, CTG	GAU, GAC
5.	Cysteine	ACA, ACG	UGU, UGC
6.	Glutamine	GTT, GTC	GAA, GAG
7.	Glutamic acid	CTT, CTC	CAA, CAG
8.	Glycine	CCA, CCG	GGU, GGC
9.	Histidine	GTA, GTG	CAU, CAC
10.	Isolucine	TAA, TAG	AUU, AUC
11.	Leucine	GAA, GAG	CUU, CUC
12.	Lysine	TTT, TTC	AAA, AAG
13.	Methionine	TAC	AUG
14.	Phenylalanine	AAA	UUU
15.	Proline	GGA, GGG	CCU, CCC
16.	Serine	AGA	UCU
17.	Threonine	TGA	ACU
18.	Tryptophan	ACC	UGG
19.	Tyrosine	ATA, ATG	UAU, UAC
20.	Valine	CAA	GUU

- The mRNA strand also contains **chain initiation** and **chain termination** codons. The codon present at the beginning of the gene is called initiation codon and usually its sequence is AUG. The initiation codon marks the beginning of the message for a polypeptide chain. The termination codon are present at the end of gene which terminates the formation of polypeptide chain and usually its sequence is UAA or UAG.
- The genetic codes are same in all kinds of living organisms whether unicellular or multicellular. As the genetic code is universal, almost any cell in any organism can read the genetic code and translate it into relevant protein. This is exactly happening by producing human insulin on an industrial scale by bacteria that have been genetically engineered to carry human insulin gene.
- Any change in the sequential arrangement of bases of a codon may lead to defective formation of protein.

TRANSCRIPTION

In the process of transcription the genetic information stored in the DNA of a gene is transmitted to messengers RNA. This is the first step in the formation of protein.

Following are the steps in the process of transcription:

- Because of the breakage of hydrogen bonds between nitrogenous base pairs, the two strands of DNA double helix are separated from each other. This is achieved by binding of RNA polymerase to the promoter region. The separation of strands takes place in the region of particular gene which is to be coded.
- The process of transcription begins with the activation of **transcription factors** and release of **RNA polymerase** in the promoter region of the gene.
- Only one strand of DNA double helix is used for synthesis of mRNA molecule.
- The mRNA is single stranded. It is synthesized by the enzyme RNA polymerase with the help of this enzyme appropriate ribo-nucleotides are added to the mRNA chain.
- The transcription begins at 5' end and ends at 3' end.
- Every base in newly synthesized mRNA molecule is complementary to a corresponding base in the DNA of the gene. The cytosine (C) pairs with guanine (G), thymine (T) with adenine (A) but adenine pairs with uracil (U). Thus information of a particular gene (DNA strand) is transferred to mRNA unchanged.
- In a strand of mRNA all the sequences of a structural gene are transcribed i.e. extrons and introns.

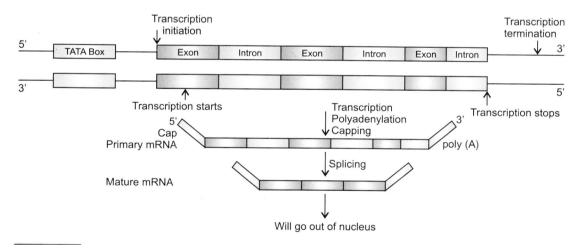

Fig. 5.2: *Transcription of mRNA from DNA, 5' end capping and 3' end polyadenylation and splicing of mRNA to get mature mRNA.*

- The intervening non coding sequences (introns) are excised. The exons are spliced together to form a mature RNA which is relatively shorter in length. This process is known as **splicing** (removal of introns by cutting them off and joining the ends of extrons).

- Molecule of methylguanine gets attached to the 5′ end and is called methylguanine cap. This 5′ cap protects the mRNA from degradation and facilitate transport of mRNA to cytoplasm.
- The 3′ end of m RNA is called poly (A) tail which also protects mRNA from degradation and facilitates the transport of mRNA to cytoplasm.
- The mRNA then migrates from nucleus to cytoplasm where it attaches to ribosomes for synthesis of protein (translation).

FURTHER DETAILS

Alternative Splicing

At one time it was taught that one gene produced only one protein or enzyme. However, it is now known that although there are only about 30,000 to 35,000 genes in the human genome, protein number more than 100,000. The mechanism by which a single gene can give rise to many proteins is as follows.

As stated earlier, a single gene can synthesized more than one protein. This is achieved by the process called **alternative splicing.** In this process, the exons are spliced in different patterns (Fig. 5.3). The absence of one or two exons in mRNA changes the sequence of amino acids present in the resulting polypeptide chain. In this way different proteins are formed by a single gene. Similarly, the function of the protein, made from the messenger RNA, can also be modified by its phosphorylation, or by its combination with other proteins. This explains why the number of proteins exceeds by almost three times the number of genes present in the human genome.

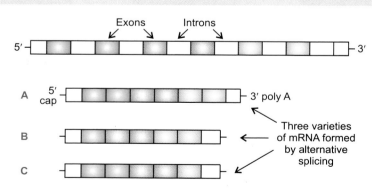

Fig. 5.3: *Diagram showing the process of alternative splicing. Transcription of a structural gene may form a mature mRNA in which all exons are present (A); where one exon is excluded in the process of splicing (B and C). Thus a single gene can form three different kinds of proteins.*

TRANSCRIPTION FACTORS

- Transcription factors play an important role in the process of transcription. They are also known as **gene regulatory proteins.**
- At present more than 30 genes are known which synthesize transcription factors.
- The transcription factors are present in the nucleus. They determine the region of the DNA to be transcribed.
- The transcription factors have special affinity to bind to DNA strand in the promoter region of the gene.
- They are capable to bind to a DNA strand because they have structural motifs. These structural motifs may be of four different types i.e., **helix-turn-helix, zinc finger, leucine zipper** and **helix-loop-helix** motifs.
- The transcription factors not only bind to the promoter region of a gene but may also bind to the enhancers and activate the speed and timing of gene expression in a specific cell.

TRANSLATION

The mRNA is synthesized by the process of "transcription". It brings the genetic information for the synthesis of polypeptide chain from the nucleus (DNA) to cytoplasm. Thus the synthesis of protein molecule (polypeptide chains), in a cell, is directed by an mRNA. The translation system consists of the following components:

1. **Messenger RNA**
   The mRNA forms the important component of the translation as it provides the coding sequence of bases that determines the sequential arrangement of amino acids in the polypeptide chain.
2. **Ribosome**
   It consists of two subunits (small and large) which come together on the mRNA strand to form a mature ribosome. The small unit reads the code on mRNA while large unit align successive tRNA molecules and helps in the attachment of amino acids one by one by the peptide bonds.
3. **Transfer RNA**
   Each specific tRNA is attached to the specific amino acid. This attachment is due to the enzyme **aminoacyl-tRNA synthetases.** A tRNA attached to its amino acid is called **charged tRNA.**
   The codon on the mRNA binds to an anticodon on tRNA. This brings the attached amino acid into line for elongation of the growing polypeptide chain.

The process of translation consists of three stages i.e., **initiation, elongation** and **termination (Fig. 5.4).**

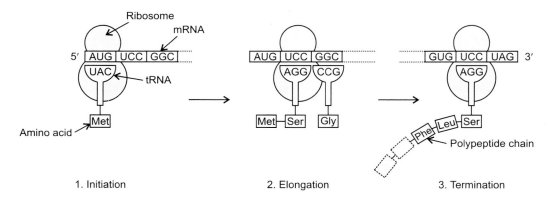

Fig. 5.4: *Stages of translation. Here the initiation of translation started with AUG and terminated with UAG.*

Initiation

- The process of initiation begins at 5′ cap on the mRNA.
- At this end, mRNA **initiation complex** is formed. This is formed by giving attachment to elongation factors (elF4, elF2, elF3 and elF5), small subunit of ribosome (40 S) and an initiator tRNA (with UAC nucleotide sequence anticodon).
- Once the initiation complex is formed it moves along the mRNA in 3′ direction, till the first AUG nucleotide sequence is encountered. The AUG nucleotide sequence acts as **start codon** that signals the start of polypeptide synthesis.
- Now large subunit (60 S) of ribosome gets attached to the small subunit. All other initiation factors are now released from the initiation complex.
- The initiator tRNA (with UAC anticodon sequence) along with its amino acid gets attached to the AUG codon in the mRNA with the help of hydrogen bonds.

Elongation

- In the first step of elongation the small subunit of ribosome moves one codon further on the mRNA. (As the small subunit of ribosome moves on the mRNA, it goes on translating the codon present on it.)
- The new activated tRNA corresponding to new codon is brought to large subunit of ribosome along with the corresponding amino acid.
- The new amino acid joins to the previous amino acid by the formation of peptide bond under the influence of **peptidyl transferase** in the large subunit of ribosome.
- Now 60 S subunit of ribosome moves forward to catch up with the small subunit (40 S).
- After formation of bond between first two amino acids one cycle of elongation is completed and the whole process is repeated for next codon.
- Thus the elongation takes place codon by codon.

Termination

- As soon as the stop codon is encountered on the mRNA strand a **release factor (RF)** binds with the ribosome.
- No new tRNA can bind to the ribosome.
- The polypeptide chain gets detached from the tRNA to which it is attached.
- Thus the function of RF is to recognize the stop codon and to release the polypeptide chain from the ribosome.
- Now the RF (release factor) is also removed from ribosome.
- The 40 S and 60 S subunit of ribosome are separated from each other and are recycled.
- Most polypeptide chains now fold and they are released from the ribosome.

On a mRNA strand several ribosome can move in tandem. These ribosomes are placed about 80 nucleotides distance from each other (after about 25 amino acids have been joined together in a polypeptide chain). This also indicates that all ribosomes attached to the mRNA move at the same speed. A large complex, where many ribosomes are attached to a single mRNA is called as polysome or **polyribosome.**

REGULATION OF GENE EXPRESSION

All the cells in the body have the same genetic constitution. They all contain the same 46 chromosomes. Then why different tissues in body synthesize different kind of proteins i.e. skin cells produce keratin, endocrine pancreas synthesize insulin and red blood cells produce haemoglobin etc? This is due to the fact that in a particular tissue (or during specific time of development) only few genes are active and others resting. Thus there exists a mechanism of control of gene expression.

Mechanism of control of gene expression in lower organisms

- Control genes are of two different kinds i.e. **regulator gene** and **operator gene.**
- An operator gene is situated adjacent to the structural genes in the chromosome. The structural genes are under the control of operator genes which stimulate their activity. The unit of operator gene and structural genes is called as **operon** (Fig. 5.5).
- A regulator gene controls the operator gene and is usually away from operon. The regulator gene synthesizes **repressor**

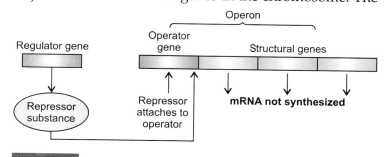

Fig. 5.5: *The repressor substance produced by regulator gene inhibits operator gene. Thus structural genes become inactive and proteins are not synthesized.*

substance which inhibits operator gene which in turn inhibits structural gene. Thus when regulator gene is functioning proteins are not synthesized by structural genes.

- On the other hand, some enzymes or metabolites may combine with repressor substance and prevents it action on operator gene. The derepressed operator gene then stimulates structural genes which synthesize proteins (Fig. 5.6).

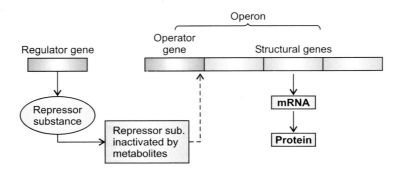

Fig. 5.6: *As repressor substance is inactivated by metabolites, operator gene is not inhibited. Thus structural genes can synthesize protein.*

- In higher organisms regulation of transcription is more complex and specific to certain tissue or cell types through the action of hormones or growth factors. Regulation of transcription is effected through binding of **transcription factor** to specific DNA elements in **promoter region**. This region includes TATA, CAT boxes etc. (Fig. 5.1). There are DNA sequences which are known to increase the level of transcription and are called **"enhancers"**. Similarly, there are also regions which inhibit transcription and are called **"silencers"**.

MUTATION

Mutation may be defined as *the heritable changes in the genetic material of an individual.* The term genetic material is a broad term which includes, at one end, the smallest unit of a gene i.e. "nucleotide" and at other end "a set of chromosomes." Thus mutation may occur in a single gene or in chromosome(s).

- If heritable change occurs in the structure of a gene then it is called as **gene mutation** or **point mutation**.
- When change occurs is chromosomes (structural or numerical) then it is referred as **chromosomal mutation**.
- However, the term mutation is mostly used for gene mutation only. The numerical and structural abnormalities of chromosomes are presented in Chapter 6. In this chapter we shall deal only with gene or point mutation.

- Mutation is seen in all living organism. It is ultimate source of all genetic variations.
- Mutation is essential for long term survival of any species. Without mutation a species can not acquire new genes which are necessary for adaptation in changing environment. Thus *mutation provides raw material for evolution*.
- However, most mutations are harmful.

Somatic and Germinal mutation

- If the mutation occurs in somatic cell then it is called somatic mutation and if it occurs in germ cell (egg or sperm) it is known as germinal mutation.
- Germ line mutations are inherited but somatic mutations are not. The somatic mutation can not be transmitted to offspring while germinal mutation occurs in germ cell hence is transmitted to next generation.
- Somatic mutation produces local phenotypical change in that individual while germinal mutation will show generalized effect on that individual.
- Individuals with somatic mutation are mosaics (they will have genetically two different types of cells). In case of germinal mutation, as mutation is transmitted through a sperm or egg, the resulting offspring will not be mosaic because all its cells will carry the mutation.

"Loss of function mutation" and "Gain of function mutation"

Mutation usually leads to the loss of function of that gene. However, sometimes mutation may lead to acquisition of new function or increased level of gene expression.

If the mutation results in either the complete inactivation of gene (elimination of the function of gene) or reduced activity of the gene then it is called as **"loss of function mutation"**. This is also known as **"knockout"** or **"null"** mutation. Most of the loss of function mutations is recessive.

The **"gain of function mutation"** results either in the over expression of gene (gene product is over produced) or it may become active in type of tissue in which gene is not normally active. Most of the "gain of function mutation" is dominant. When these mutations occur in homozygous state they manifest as sever disorder e.g. homozygous achondroplasia. Most mutations that lead to over expression of gene are responsible for cancer (Chapter 11).

Molecular Basis of Gene Mutation (Point mutation)

Though the process of replication of DNA is very accurate but, sometimes alteration may take place in the arrangement of nucleotides in a polynucleotide chain of DNA molecule. These changes are not visible in the microscope but have various phenotypic effects on individual. These smallest changes may involve the addition, deletion or substitution of a single nucleotide pair in the DNA molecule.

Point mutations (gene mutations) are of following types:

1. Substitution mutations.
2. Frame shift mutation (deletion or insertion mutation).

Substitution mutation

This is relatively common kind of mutation. In this kind of mutation one nitrogenous base of a triplet code of DNA is replaced by another nitrogenous base. This changes the codon which may code for different amino acid. For example in sickle cell anemia, in GAG triplet code of mRNA (which codes for glutamic acid) if base A is replaced by U, at the time of transcription, then code GUG will produce valine amino acid instead of glutamic acid. This one different amino acid in a polypeptide chain will lead to the formation of altered protein. The defective B-globin polypeptide chain will form needle like crystals and will deform RBCs. The effect of deformed RBCs may be seen as many abnormalities throughout the body.

The substitution mutation may or may not be lethal. As there occurs the replacement of only one amino acid in the polypeptide chain which might not produce any significant change. Such mutations are known as **silent mutations**. However, on other hand, in sickle cell anemia there occurs the substitution of single nucleotide which leads to serious disease. However sometimes gene mutation may be beneficial also. For beneficial effects of sickle cell mutation refer Chapter 9.

Frame shift mutation

This type of mutation is due to insertion or deletion of nitrogenous base in DNA or mRNA. This leads to the shifting of reading frame of codon from the site of change onward (Fig. 5.7).

A frame shift mutation may involve the addition or deletion of one, two or more nucleotides. Frame shift mutations are often lethal because all the triplet codes beyond the point of mutation are misread. This will ultimately leads to the synthesis of highly altered protein.

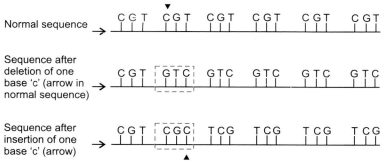

Fig. 5.7: *Frame shift mutation which leads to the change in the triplet genetic code.*

Mutagens

Mutations can occur naturally where no cause can be detected. These kinds of mutations are called **spontaneous** mutations. These are usually due to errors in DNA replication. Mutations are also known to occur due to exposure to environmental agents. These agents are known as **mutagens**.

There are two types of mutagens:

1. **Chemical and physical mutagens**:
   Many chemicals like mustard gas, formaldehyde, benzene, thalidomide and L.S.D. are considered as mutagenic in animals. Physical agent like high temperature is a known mutagenic agent in animals.

2. **Radiation**
   Both natural and artificial ionizing radiations are known to cause mutation. Natural radiations that come from cosmic rays of the sun (natural sunlight) and UV lamps are the source of mutations. The other source of natural radiation is the radioactive elements like thorium, radium and uranium present in earth.

   Artificial ionizing radiation includes X-rays, gamma rays, alpha and beta rays (particles) and neutrons. The effect of ionizing radiations on chromosomes is severe. It causes break in the chromosomes and chromatids. These breaks are due to involvement of sugar phosphate backbone of polynucleotide strand. This leads to various kinds of structural and numerical abnormalities in chromosomes (Ch. 6).

DNA REPAIR

In human cells, the spontaneous damage to the DNA caused by chemical and radiation is quite high. In every human cell, the DNA is damaged at 10,000 different sites during the period of 24 hours. However, most of these damages are automatically repaired by various molecular mechanisms. The most common mechanisms of DNA repair are as under:

- The nick in the DNA strand is repaired by the enzyme **DNA ligase.**
- At the site where base has been lost the repair is executed with the help of enzyme **AP endonuclease.**
- At the site where relatively a large part of DNA strand (few base pairs) is damaged the repair is executed in various steps. The damaged part of DNA strand is cleaved by the enzyme **endonuclease.** The damaged portion is then removed by enzyme **exonuclease.** The portion of newly synthesized DNA strand is inserted with the help of enzyme **DNA polymerase.** Ultimately break is sealed by **DNA ligase**.
- The repair of DNA caused by ultraviolet light is achieved by the product of at least eight genes.

SUMMARY

Gene

- The structural gene is defined as *"a segment of DNA which contains the information (code) for synthesis of one complete polypeptide chain"*. Thus gene provides instruction for making a specific protein.
- The control genes regulate the activity of structural genes.
- The DNA portion of a structural gene not only contains coding sequences for amino acids (**exons**) but also contains non-coding sequences (**introns**).
- A structural gene also contains flanking regions at the ends which are important for regulation of gene.

Genetic code

- Protein is made up of polypeptide chains which in turn are made up of amino acids.
- A sequence of three bases on DNA strand codes for one amino acid.
- Thus a portion of DNA strand that constitute a structural gene contains the sequentially arranged codes for all the amino acids which forms a complete polypeptide chain.

Transcription

- In this process the genetic information stored in DNA (in the form of triplet code) of a gene is transmitted to messenger RNA.
- As the base pairing is rigid the information of DNA strand is transferred to mRNA unchanged.

Transcription factors

- Transcription factors (gene regulatory proteins) play an important role in the process of transcription.
- Transcription factors bind to the DNA strand in the promoter region of the gene.
- They determine the region of the DNA to be transcribed.

Translation

- Translation is the process of synthesis of polypeptide chain as per the arrangement of the codes on the mRNA.
- In this process mRNA gets attached to the ribosomes.
- The small unit of ribosome reads the code on mRNA while large unit align successive tRNA.
- Each specific tRNA is attached to the specific amino acid. These attached amino acids are brought into line for elongation of the growing polypeptide chain as per the codon on the mRNA.

Regulation of gene expression

- Function of control genes is to regulate the structural genes.
- Control genes are of two different kinds i.e. regulator gene and operator gene.
- The unit of operator gene and structural gene is called operon.
- Regulator gene synthesizes repressor substance which inhibits operator gene which inturn inhibits structural genes.
- Some metabolites may combine with repressor substance so that operator gene is not inhibited.
- In higher organisms regulation of transcription is more complex.

Mutation

- *The heritable changes in the genetic material of an individual* is defined as mutation.
- Mutation may occur in a gene (point mutation or gene mutation) or it may occur in chromosome (chromosomal mutation).
- Point mutations are either **substitution** mutation or **frame shift** mutation.
- The point mutation is due to addition, deletion or substitution of a single nucleotide in the DNA molecule.
- If mutation occurs in somatic cell it is called as **somatic mutation** and if it occurs in germ cell it is called **germinal mutation**.
- The environmental agents like chemicals and radiations may also cause mutations. These agents are called **mutagens**.

6 Chromosome Disorders

- Disorders of Chromosome Number
- Disorders of Chromosome Structure
- Mosaicism / Chimaerism

It is important for an individual to have all 46 chromosomes (with all the normal genes) for a healthy life. If the balance of genes is disturbed by the absence or addition of few genes (even if these genes are normal and not mutated), this will upset the normal process of development. The balance of genes can be disturbed by chromosomal abnormalities which are of following types:

- Disorders of chromosome number.
- Disorders of chromosome structure.
- Different cell lines (Mosaicism/Chimaerism).

Chromosome abnormalities are responsible for significant morbidity and mortality in humans. These abnormalities are responsible for:

- more than 50% of spontaneous abortions.
- up to 1% of congenital and childhood disabilities
- malignancy

DISORDERS OF CHROMOSOME NUMBER

This abnormality arises because an individual may have more (47, 48 .... etc.) or less (45) number of chromosomes instead of normal 46. A cell with a missing chromosome would have 45 chromosomes and the condition is called as **monosomy** (because in this condition one particular chromosome is single and not in pair). For example in Turner's syndrome, (XO) female has only one X chromosome instead of XX. When a cell has three copies of a chromosome instead of two the condition is called as **trisomy**. Similarly, if an individual has four copies of same chromosome it is designated as **tetrasomy**. The tetrasomy of autosomes is not known in human. However, tetrasomy of sex chromosome (XXXX) is sometimes observed.

Another kind of numerical abnormality of chromosome is called **polyploidy**. In this condition, the number of chromosomes in a somatic cell increases by one or two complete set of chromosomes. A complete set of chromosomes consists of twenty-two autosomes and one sex chromosome. This is called **haploid**. The chromosomes in all human gametes are haploid in number (23). A normal somatic cell contains two haploid sets of chromosomes (46) hence, called as **diploid**. Similarly, cells that have three haploid sets of chromosomes (69) are called **triploid** and with four haploid sets (92) are called **tetraploid**.

FURTHER DETAILS

How abnormality occurs in chromosome number?

At the time of spermatogenesis or oogenesis it may so happen that an egg or a sperm may have both the members of homologous pair of chromosome instead of only one; or a gamete may lack one particular chromosome. These abnormal gametes are formed during meiosis, because members of one of the pair of chromosome fail to separate from each other and migrate to opposite poles.

The failure of homologous pair of chromosomes to separate during meiosis I is called **non-disjunction**. Similarly, non-disjunction may also occur during meiosis-II when a pair of sister chromatids fails to separate. Both these types of non-disjunction are shown in Fig. 6.1.

Trisomy

The two chromosomes of a pair may go to same pole during first meiotic division (Fig. 6.1A). Similarly, during meiosis II a pair of sister chromatids may go to same pole (Fig. 6.1B). The resulting gamete then has 24 chromosomes instead of normal 23. At fertilization by this gamete, the zygote will, therefore, have 47 chromosomes, there being three identical chromosomes. This is called **trisomy** (Fig. 6.2a).

Monosomy

When both chromosomes of a pair go to one gamete (as above), the other gamete resulting from the division has only 22 chromosome (instead of normal 23). At fertilization zygote has only 45 chromosomes. Hence, one pair is represented by a single chromosome. It is called **monosomy** (Fig. 6.2b).

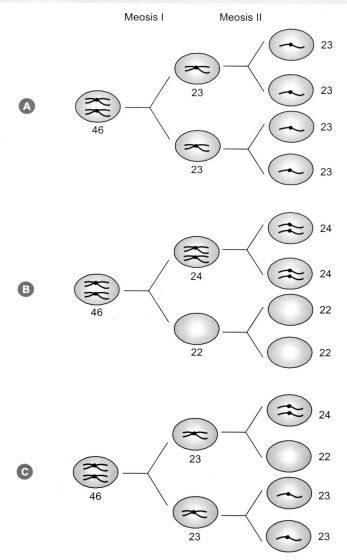

Meosis I   Meosis II

Fig. 6.1: **A.** *Normal gametogenesis - showing normal separation of single pair of chromosomes during meiosis I and II. Numbers indicate total number of chromosomes.*
B. *This shows the failure of separation of homologous chromosomes during meiosis I. Out of the four gametes which are formed at the end of meiosis II, two have an extra chromosome while in other two the particular chromosome is missing.*
C. *This shows the failure of separation of sister chromatids during meosis II. Thus out of the four gametes one contain extra chromosome, one with absence of that particular chromosome and remaining two gametes are normal.*

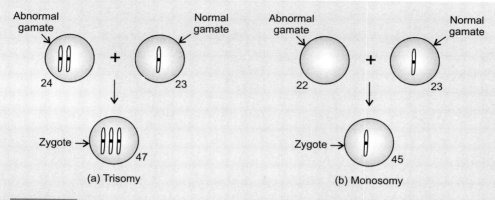

Fig. 6.2: *(a) Diagram showing zygote containing three identical chromosomes (trisomy). Total number of chromosome in this zygote are 47.*
(b) Diagram showing monosomy.

Non-disjunction is not only seen during gametogenesis (meiosis) but also in developing zygote where cells are dividing mitotically. As a result of non-disjunction in the developing zygote two or more different cell lines are observed. This phenomenon is known as **mosaicism** (see below). The multiple of the haploid number of chromosomes (triploidy, 69 or tetraploidy, 92) are unknown in human. Most of triploidy result in spontaneous abortion but few may survive till birth.

What are the causes of non-disjunction?

- *Advancing maternal age*:
  The relationship between advancing maternal age and chromosomal abnormalities specially trisomy 21 (Down's syndrome), trisomy 13 and 18 are well established. The meiosis I begins in primary oocytes before birth and is completed at the time of ovulation. Thus a primary oocyte may remain in suspended activity till 45 years of age whence it undergoes meiosis II. The ageing effect is probably due to suspended inactivity of primary oocyte for many years. This may predispose to non-disjunction because of abnormality in spindle formation.
- *Radiation may be responsible for non-disjunction.*
- *Delayed fertilization after ovulation.*
- *Chemicals in the environment: smoking, alcohol consumption, oral contraceptive, fertility drugs, pesticides etc.*
- *Non-disjunction may also be under genetic control.*

Numerical Abnormalities of Autosomes

Following three trisomies are commonly observed among live-born children. **a.** trisomy 21, **b.** trisomy 13 and **c.** trisomy 18. Most other autosomal trisomies and monosomies are so severe that they result in spontaneous abortion.

TRISOMY 21: DOWN'S SYNDROME OR MONGOLISM

Incidence: 1 in 700 live-birth. Incidence increases with the advancing maternal age (at the 45 years of age incidence is as high as 1 in 16). Males are more affected than females.

Clinical features:
- Affected children are mentally retarded - I.Q. scores range from 25 to 75.
- Poor growth, short stature and poor muscle tone.
- Approximately 40% of children suffer from major heart defects.
- Facial features are typical-small head circumference, epicanthic fold, protruding tongue, small ears and slopping palpebral fissures.
- Hands are short and broad. There may be simian crease (single palmar crease resulting because of fusion of heart and head lines).

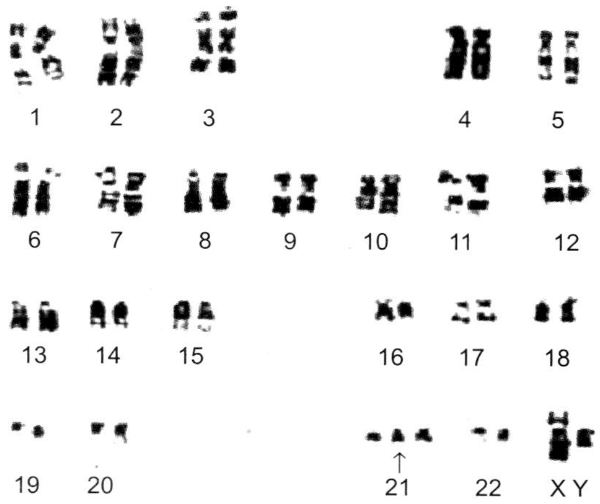

Fig. 6.3: *Karyotype of Down's Syndrome (47, XY + 21) (Courtesy of Prof. Sayee Rajangam, St. John's Medical College, Bangalore)*

Genotype:

Down's syndrome may be because of following chromosomal abnormalities.

- Trisomy
- Translocation
- Mosaicism

Trisomy of chromosome 21 is most common cause (95%) of Down's syndrome. Genotype in trisomy is either 47+XY or 47+XX. The extra 21 chromosome is mostly due to non-disjunction during maternal meiosis I. Robertsonian translocation (see below) may be the cause of Down's syndrome in 3% cases. The genotype is 46+XX

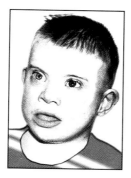

Fig. 6.4a: *Note the typical facial features of Down's syndrome i.e., small head circumference, protruding tongue, small ear and slopping palpebral fissure. Courtesy "www.msu.edu".*

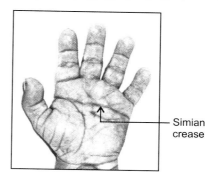

— Simian crease

Fig. 6.4b: *Short and broad hand showing simian crease. Courtesy "www.msu.edu".*

or 46+XY. Children with mosaicism have two cell lines (normal and trisomic) hence, less severely affected.

Life span: The mean age is 16 years though it varies from few weeks to decades. Most affected adults develop Alzheimer's disease in later life.

Recurrence risk: The risk of a subsequent child having Down's syndrome, when one child is already affected, increases with the age of mother. The risk is three times more as compared to woman of same age, who has not previously had an affected child.

In case of translocation, if father is a carrier then the recurrence risk is 1-3% but risk increases to 15% in case of carrier mother.

Counselling:

The prenatal diagnosis of Down's syndrome can be made by following methods.

- **Amniocentesis** for chromosomal analysis is advisable (Ch. 14).
- **The triple test:** In this test the three biochemical markers (α-fetoprotein, oestriol and chorionic gonadotrophin) present in maternal serum are tested at 16 weeks gestation. In Down's syndrome pregnancies the level of α-fetoprotein and oestriol level tend to be reduced as compared to normal, while the level of human chorionic gonadotrophin increased.
- The level of **inhibin-A** also increases in maternal serum.

TRISOMY 13: PATAU'S SYNDROME

Incidence: Most of these trisomies lead to spontaneous abortion. The incidence among the live-birth is 1 in 5000. Most of the affected children die within a month and none of them survive more than 3 or 4 months after birth.

Clinical features:
- Affected children are physically and mentally retarded.
- They have small skull and eyes.
- They may have cleft lip and cleft palate.
- They may born with extra finger or malformed thumb.
- Malformations of CVS, CNS and excretory systems are common.

Genotype:
- Trisomy of chromosome 13.
- Mosaicism & Robertsonian translocation are observed in rare cases.

Counselling:
- There is small risk of recurrence.
- Incidence increases with advanced maternal age.

TRISOMY 18: EDWARD'S SYNDROME

Incidence:
- Most cases of this trisomy result into spontaneous abortion.
- It occurs in about 1 in 6500 live birth. Early death (before 6 months of age) is characteristic feature. However, sometimes, long term survivals may also be seen.

Clinical features:
- Retarded growth and development
- Hypertonia
- Prominent large head (occiput)
- Low set malformed ears
- Small chin
- Child holds fingers in typical way due to abnormal insertion of tendons.
- Heart defects (ventricular septal defects and patent ductus arteriosus) are commonly seen.

Genotype:
Trisomy of chromosome 18.

Counselling:
Though there is maternal age effect but it is considered as sporadic event hence, risk of recurrence is less.

Numerical abnormalities of sex chromosomes

Following numerical abnormalities of sex chromosomes are commonly seen

- Trisomies like XXY, XYY or XXX
- Monosomy like 45, XO
- Mosaicism, 46, XY/46, XX

An extra X or Y chromosome usually has a relatively mild effect. This is because Y chromosome contains relatively few functional genes and in each somatic cell except one X chromosome all others form bar bodies.

TURNER SYNDROME, 45, XO

Incidence:

- This abnormality (monosomy) is a common cause of spontaneous abortion. About 20% of spontaneously aborted fetuses have 45, XO genotype.
- Incidence of live-born infants varies from 1 in 5000 to 1 in 10,000. They survive to develop into individual having **Turner's syndrome**.

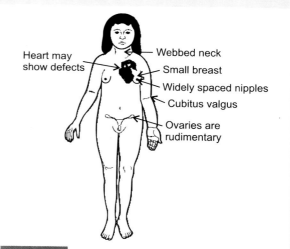

Clinical features:

Affected individual is a female with following features:

- Affected female is of normal intelligence or slightly retarded.
- They may show webbed neck, low posterior hair line, cubitus valgus, broad chest with widely spaced nipples. They are of short stature.
- They have specific defects in arithmetical skills, reading the maps and drawing the diagrams.
- They may show ventricular septal defects or coarctation of aorta.
- Various abnormalities of urinary system may be seen.

Fig. 6.5: *Clinical features of Turner syndrome also include short height, low posterior hair line and absence of menstruation.*

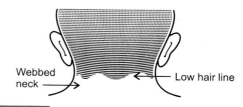

Fig. 6.6: *The back of neck showing hair arising from lower portion of neck.*

- Patients are mostly sterile which is due to failure of ovaries to develop. This also leads to absence of menstruation. Breasts fail to develop and pubic hair are scanty.

Genotype:

- Monosomy of X chromosome (45, XO) is the most frequent cause of Turner's syndrome.
- Mosaicism - 45, XO/46, XX
- Isochromosome - 46,X,i(Xq)
- Ring chromosome - 46, X,r(X)
- Sex-chromatin examination is always negative as there is only one X chromosome.

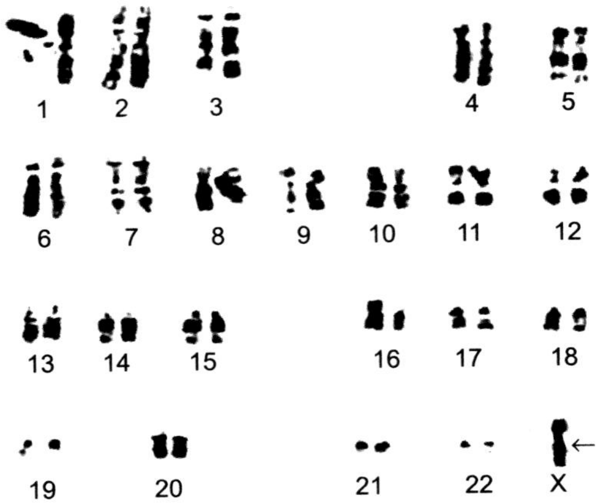

Counselling:

- Oestrogen replacement therapy should be given at adolescence for development of secondary sexual characteristics.
- Though affected females are sterile but can bear child with the help of "**In vitro fertilization**".

Fig. 6.7: *Turner syndrome (45, X). (Courtesy of Prof. Sayee Rajangam, St. John's Medical College, Bangalore)*

47, XXX FEMALES

Incidence:

- 0.1% of all females

Clinical features:

- They are phenotypically normal.
- I.Q. of affected females is close to normal.
- They have normal reproductive life.

Genotype:

- Chromosomal examination shows XXX chromosome. They show two Barr bodies. (Females with more than 3X chromosomes can also survive i.e. 48, XXXX and 49, XXXXX. However, these females are sterile, severely mentally retarded and have many phenotypic defects.)

47, XXY: KLINEFELTER SYNDROME

Incidence:

- It occurs in 1 per 1000 new born males.

Clinical features:

- The sex of affected individual is male.
- Syndrome can not be detected until adolescence age. He usually attends clinic as married person for infertility.
- Though the appearance of person is normal he is tall and have some degree of mental retardation.
- Affected individual has very small testes but normal penis and scrotum.
- Puberty fails to occur normally.
- Secondary sexual characters doesn't develop fully and the pubic and facial hair are scanty. Gynaecomestia (inlarged breast) is seen in some cases.

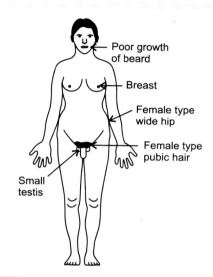

Fig. 6.8: *Person affected from Klinefelter syndrome is infertile due to small testis. He may have inlarged breast.*

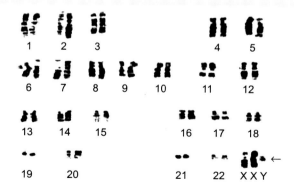

Fig. 6.9: *Karyotype of Klinefelter syndrome (47, XXY). (Courtesy of Prof. Sayee Rajangam, St. John's Medical College, Bangalore)*

Genotype:

- Karyotype is 47, XXY
- Mosaicism - 46XY/47, XXY
  These individuals show Barr body.

Counselling:

- At the age of puberty, the treatment with testosterone will help to develop the secondary sexual character.

47, XYY MALES

Incidence: 1 in 1000 newborns.

Clinical features:

- Phenotypically they are normal but usually they are tall.
- Slight mental retardation is always associated.
- Contrary to common belief most of them are not criminal
- They show emotional immaturity and impulsive behaviours.

Genotype:

- Karyotype - 47, XYY. The additional Y chromosome is usually due to non-disjunction of meiosis II during spermatogenesis.

DISORDERS OF CHROMOSOME STRUCTURE

Most common structural abnormalities refer to chromosomes that have a portion missing or a portion represented twice. The abnormalities in structure of chromosomes result because of **chromosome breakage**. The chromosomes are highly fragile and they may sometimes break spontaneously. Some external factors like **X-rays**, **chemicals**, and **viral infections** are also responsible for chromosome breakage. Those fragments of chromosomes which have no centromere are lost during cell division as they can not moves to poles in daughter cells. Only those abnormal chromosomes which have centromere will persist and may be transmitted to next generation. Following are the important structural abnormalities.

- Deletion
- Inversion
- Ring chromosome
- Isochromosome
- Translocation

The structural abnormalities are responsible for various types of disorders. This is because loss of genes (as in deletion), gain of genes (as in duplication) and also because of change in the normal position of genes (as in inversion and translocation).

KARYOTYPE SYMBOLS

p	Short arm of chromosome
q	Long arm of chromosome
ter	Terminal portion
qter	Terminal portion of long arm
pter	Terminal porton of short arm
+	Before number of chromosome indicates that chromosome or arm is extra e.g. +21.
—	Chromosome or arm is missing.
dup	Duplication
Mos	Mosaic
/	Separates karyotypes in mosaics e.g. 47, XXX/45, X
del	Deletion
inv	Inversion
r	Ring chromosome
i	Isochromosome
rep	Reciprocal translocation
rob	Robertsonian translocation

Deletion

In this kind of structural abnormality breakage occurs in a part of chromosome and broken part is subsequently lost as it has no centromere.

The part of a chromosome may delete near it terminal end by a single break. Sometimes an intervening portion may delete by two breaks (Fig. 6.10). There may be several genes within deleted portion of the chromosome. An individual can not survive if a large part chromosome is deleted. A loss of more than 2% of genome will be lethal. Deletions are of two kinds.

a. *Microscopic or chromosomal deletion*

This can be visualized microscopically by usual karyotyping if the deletion is quite large e.g. deletion of short arm of chromosome 5(cri-du-chat syndrome) and short arm of chromosome 4 (Wolf-Hirschhorn syndrome) are well known examples.

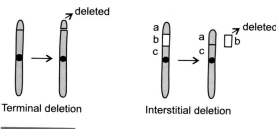

Terminal deletion   Interstitial deletion

Fig. 6.10: *Types of microscopic deletion.*

CRI-DU-CHAT SYNDROME

Incidence: 1 in 50,000 births

Genetics: This syndrome is due to deletion of short arm of chromosome 5 (5p-).

Clinical features:

- The affected new born suffer from underdevelopment of Larynx hence they make characteristic cat like cry.
- Syndrome is associated with microcephaly, physical and mental retardation.
  (Similarly, infants suffering from Wolf-Hirschhorn (4p-) are severally mentally retarded and may also show the retarded physical growth).

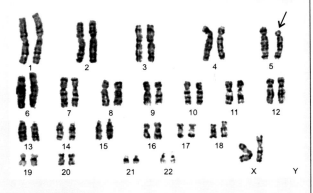

Fig. 6.11: *Karyotype of Cri-du-chat syndrome.*

b. *Submicroscopic microdeletions*

This can not be visualized by usual karyotype but needs FISH studies. Following is the list of common microdeletion syndromes.

Syndrome	Affected chromosome number
Prader-Willi	15
Angelman	15
Wilms tumour	11
Williams	7
Langer Giedion	8
Miller-Dieker	17
Di-George	22

Inversion

This abnormality involves only a single chromosome which breaks at two points. The broken segment rearranges itself by inverting its position. The inversion abnormality is of two different types i.e. pericentric and paracentric, as shown in Fig. 6.12.

Pericentric inversion

Paracentric inversion

Fig. 6.12: *Types of inversion*

Inversion abnormalities are not responsible for any clinical problems in carriers. This is due to the fact that no chromosomal material is lost. However, if an important functional gene is disrupted at the site of break it may cause problem. A chromosome with inversion gives rise to abnormal gametes because during meiosis I there is formation of unbalanced recombinant chromosomes. This leads to spontaneous abortions or abnormal offspring.

Ring chromosomes

This is a rare abnormality where chromosome forms a closed circle (ring). Ring chromosome results because of breaks near tips (ends) on each arm. These broken and sticky ends subsequently fuse with each other (Fig. 6.13). The two distal fragments are lost during cell division. Sister chromatid exchange during mitosis in a ring chromosome leads to abnormal configuration, because of which entire chromosome

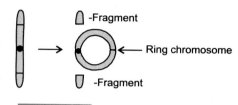

Fig. 6.13: *Ring chromosome.*

is usually lost from the cell. Therefore, individuals with a ring chromosome are usually chromosomal mosaics.

Isochromosomes

This kind of chromosome results because of incorrect splitting of centromere (Fig. 6.14). The splitting results in two isochromosomes that has two genetically identical arms. In a cell with an isochromosome there will be a duplication of one entire chromosome arm and a deletion of the other chromosome arm.

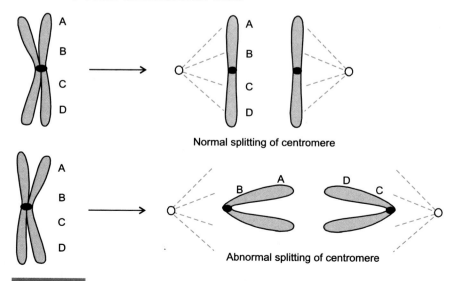

Fig. 6.14: *Formation of isochromosomes.*

Translocation

In this structural abnormality of chromosome there occurs the exchange of genetic material between two chromosomes. Translocation can be balanced or unbalanced. The carriers of balanced tanslocations are normal themselves, but their children may be physically and mentally handicapped.

Translocations are of two types:

a. *Reciprocal translocations*

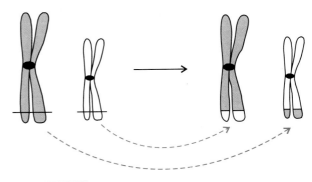

Incidence: 1 in 500 people. This translocation occurs between two non-homologous chromosomes after breakage and exchange of the fragments (Fig. 6.15). Reciprocal translocations are usually balanced rearrangements that usually have no detectable phenotypic effects in carrier. The reciprocal translocation between chromosome 11 and 22 are relatively common.

Fig. 6.15: *Reciprocal translocation.*

In reciprocal translocation problem arises at the time of gametogenesis in carrier. During meiosis I the chromosome bearing translocation can not pair normally to form bivalents, hence, they align in complicated manner. Because of this at the end of meiosis I they may segregate abnormally which leads to gametes acquiring unbalanced chromosome complement.

b. *Robertsonian translocation*

Incidence: 1 in 1000 people. This translocation results because of break at or near the centromere in two acrocentric chromosomes and subsequent fusion of their long arms.

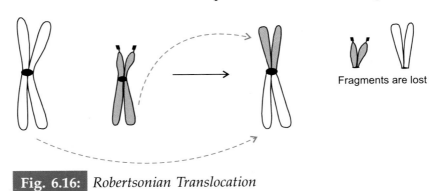

Fragments are lost

Fig. 6.16: *Robertsonian Translocation*

The short arms of both the chromosomes are lost (Fig. 6.16). This translocation most commonly occurs between chromosomes 13 and 14 (13q 14q). This is a functionally balanced translocation though chromosome number is reduced to 45. This is due to the fact that two short arms which are lost do not carry important genetic material.

Almost about 4% cases of Down's syndrome are due to Robertsonian translocation. Down's syndrome can result by inheriting two normal chromosomes 21 (one each from mother and father) and one translocated chromosome involving 21 (e.g. 14q 21q).

Functionally balanced carriers of this translocation (e.g. 13q 21q or 14q 21q) runs a risk upto 10% of having a baby with Down's syndrome. However, in case of 21q 21q Robertsonian translocation all live born children suffer from Down's syndrome.

MOSAICISM/CHIMAERISM

Chromosomal Mosaic or Mosaicism

Most of the people have same chromosomal constitution in all of their cells and tissues. However, a chromosomal mosaic is an individual who has two or more cell lines i.e. one chromosome constitution in some cells and a different chromosome constitution in other cells. In mosaicism the two different cell lines are derived from a single zygote. In mosaic some of the cells may be normal (46, XX or XY) whereas others may have an extra chromosome. (47, XX or XY), suppose, if individual is male then his mosaic karyotyype will be represented as 46, XY/47, XY.

Causes of Mosaicism

The most usual cause of chromosomal mosaicism is non-disjunction occuring in an embryonic mitotic division.

Mosaicism not only occurs at chromosomal level but it may also occur at gene level. If mutation in a gene occurs in an early embryonic cell division then the foetus would have two different cell lines i.e. some cells with normal gene and other cells with mutant gene.

Chimaera

If the cells from two or more early embryos of different mouses are mixed together and introduced into the uterus of a foster mother, then this mass of cells will give rise to a normal mouse. However, this mouse has different cell lines as genetically distinct embryos have contributed to it makeup. Thus chimaera is an individual who have two or more genetically distinct cell lines which are derived from more than one zygote.

The cause of chimaerism may be the fusion of two zygotes which were obtained by fertilization of two different ova from two different sperms. This fused zygote would give rise to an embryo who will have two different cell lines. If the two zygote are of different sexes, the chimeric embryo may develop into an individual with 46,XY/46,XX genotype (true hermaphrodite).

The difference between mosaicism and chimarism is that in case of a mosaic cell lines are derived from a single zygote but in case of a chimaera different cell lines are derived because of fusion of different zygotes.

SUMMARY

Numerical Abnormalities

- The abnormalities in chromosome number may arise due to increase (47, 48... etc) or decrease (45) in number of chromosomes instead of normal 46.
- Abnormality in chromosome number usually occur during gametogenesis when homologous pair of chromosomes fails to separate from each other during meiosis I. This phenomenon is called as **non disjunction.**
- Following are the most commonly observed numerical chromosomal abnormalities.
    - Down's syndrome (trisomy 21)
    - Patau's syndrome (trisomy 13)
    - Edward's syndrome (trisomy 18)
    - Turner syndrome (45, X)
    - Klinefelter syndrome (47, XXY)
    - XXX Females
    - XYY Males

Structural Abnormalities

- Abnormalities in chromosome structure may be because of a portion of chromosome is either missing or represented twice.
- Structural abnormalities occur due to the breakage in chromosome.
- Following are the most commonly observed structural abnormalities
    - Deletion
    - Inversion
    - Ring chromosome
    - Isochromosome
    - Translocation

Mosaicism

- A mosaic is an individual who has **two or more cell lines**.
- Some cells of his/her body will have one kind of chromosomal constitution while other cells will show different constitution (i.e. 46, XY/47, XY).
- The chromosomal mosaicism is due to non-disjunction occuring during early embryonic mitotic division.

Chimaera

- A chimaera is an individual who have two or more genetically distinct cell lines which are derived from more than one zygote.

7 Modes of Inheritance and Gene Disorders

- Monogenic or Mendelian Inheritance
  —Autosomal Dominant Inheritance
  —Autosomal Recessive Inheritance
  —Sex-linked Inheritance
- Mitochondrial Inheritance
- Polygenic and Multifactorial Inheritance

Before understanding the features of gene disorders it is important to know the pattern of inheritance (dominant, recessive, sex-linked etc.) of any genetic disease because of the following reasons:

- For accurate diagnosis of genetic disorders.
- To calculate the risk of the genetic disease appearing in offspring.
- To suggest the ways to prevent the genetic disorders.

The inheritance of common traits or disorders follows following patterns:

- *Monogenic ((single gene) or Mendelian inheritance.*
- *Polygenic (multiple genes) inheritance/Multifactorial inheritance.*

MONOGENIC OR MENDELIAN INHERITANCE

In this kind of inheritance the traits are determined by single gene and it follows the Mendel's laws of inheritance (Chapter 2). The single gene inheritance is further classified into:

- Autosomal inheritance
- Sex-linked inheritance

Autosomal inheritance is due to the gene present on autosome while sex-linked inheritance in determined by gene present on sex chromosome (X or Y). The autosomal inheritance is further classified into **autosomal dominant** and **autosomal recessive**. In case of autosomal dominant inheritance the gene expresses itself clinically even in single dose (heterozygous state). However, an autosomal recessive trait is manifested clinically only when gene is in double dose (homozygous state).

Sex-linked inheritance is determined by a gene present on sex chromosome (X or Y) i.e. X-linked or Y-linked.

Pedigree chart

For the investigation of genetic disorder it is important to record a family history of relatives in relation to that particular genetic disorder. The information about the health of the whole family is recorded in the form of the pedigree chart. A pedigree is a diagram showing the ancestral history of a group of relatives. Following are certain conventions used in the preparation of pedigree chart (Fig. 7.1).

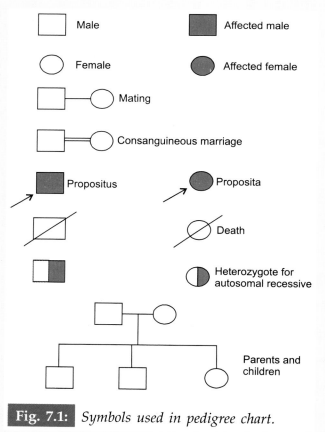

- Males are represented by squares and females by circles
- Affected persons are represented by solid squares or solid circles.
- The first individual who comes to the investigator's attention is called as proband or propositus (male) or proposita (female). The position of proband in family tree is indicated by an arrow.

Fig. 7.1: *Symbols used in pedigree chart.*

- Mating is represented by horizontal line which connects a male with a female.
- The children from a mating are represented in order of their birth from left to right.
- In the pedigree the successive generations are represented by Roman numerals e.g. I, II, III etc.

AUTOSOMAL DOMINANT INHERITANCE

The gene responsible for this kind of trait is present on autosome and can manifest the disorder even if it is in single dose (the mutant gene present on one chromosome of the pair). Following is the list of some common traits and disorders which are due to autosomal dominant inheritance.

Common baldness	Huntington's disease
Chin fissure	Myotonic dystrophy
Ear pits	Neurofibromatosis
Congenital ptosis	Hypercholesterolaemia
Epicanthus	Achondroplasia
Mid-digital hair	Polycystic kidney
ABO blood group	Congenital catract
Rh blood group	Polydactyly
Brachydactyly	

Characteristics of autosomal dominant inheritance

- Males and females are equally affected with the traits. (The transmission between all sexes are observed i.e. male to male ; female to female ; female to male and male to female.) This indicates that the gene responsible for the trait is present on autosome. Fig. 7.2 shows that both sexes are affected by the disorder.
- The trait or disorder is seen in every generation without skipping.
- An affected person will always have an affected parent. If it is not so and disorder is seen for the first time in pedigree then it is suggestive of new autosomal dominant mutation. The new mutation usually occurs at the time of gametogenesis in parents.
- Normal offsprings of the pedigree do not transmit the disorder to next generation as they do not have the abnormal gene (Fig. 7.2).

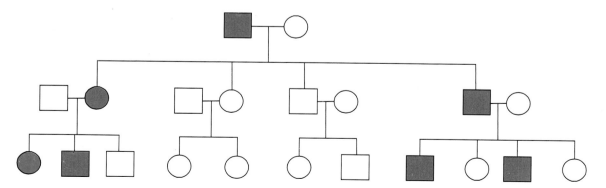

Fig. 7.2: *Pedigree chart of autosomal dominant inheritance.*

- The number of normal and affected children, in a generation, is almost in equal proportion.

Further explanation

The above characteristics can be explained as under. For each character there are two genes present on a pair of homologous chromosomes at the same locus. If one of them is a mutant gene then it will be transmitted to 50% of gametes and will express itself as it is a dominant gene. If suppose we represent the normal gene as "**a**" and mutant gene as "**A**" then genotype of normal parent will be "aa" and affected parent will be "Aa". The genetic risk can be obtained by Punnett squares (Figs. 7.3 and 7.4).

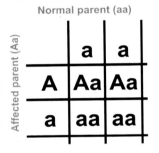

A = Mutant gene
a = Normal gene
Aa = 50% (Heterozygous affected)
aa = 50% (Homozygous normal)

Fig. 7.3: *Mating between normal (aa) and affected (Aa) parents (Aa × aa).*

The homozygous affected offspring (AA) would be severely affected as mutant genes are in double dose (Fig. 7.4).

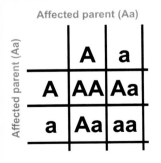

AA = 25% Severely affected
Aa = 50% Affected
aa = 25% Normal

Fig. 7.4: *Mating between two affected (Aa) parents (Aa × Aa).*

Usually the expression of gene follows the above characteristics. However, sometimes the expression of a gene does not follow above characteristics and expresses differently:

- **Pleiotrophy**

  Usually an autosomal dominant gene has one effect thus involves only one organ or part of body. However, when single gene disorder produces multiple phenotypic effect then it is called pleiotrophy. For example, in case of osteogenesis imperfecta the mutant gene is responsible for defect in the synthesis of collagen. However, the formation of defective collagen leads to many other effects like osteosclerosis, blue sclera and brittle bone etc.

- **Variable expressivity of gene**

  The phenotypic expression of an autosomal dominant gene can vary from person to person. In clinical terms the expression of gene may be in mild, moderate or severe form of the trait. One common example is polydactyly (extra finger). In some individual this extra finger may be fully formed while in other individual it may be very small.

- **Reduced or incomplete penetrance**

  It is the extreme end of variable expressivity. In this condition a person who is heterozygous for a dominant disorder fails to manifest the disorder clinically. Thus it may appear as if the disorder has skipped the generation. The penetrance of a gene in any generation is expressed in terms of percentage (%) which is calculated from the number of offspring showing the trait as compared to expected.

  The cause of reduced penetrance or the variation in the expression of gene may be due to influence of genes at other loci. It may be also due to difference in environmental factors.

- **Sex limited traits**

  Here the expression of trait is limited to one sex. The expression of sex limited traits in humans is growth of facial hair which normally occurs only in males and development of breast which occurs normally in females.

- **Sex influenced traits**

  A trait is said to be sex influenced when it expresses differently in males and females. For example, the expression of common baldness is different in males and females. It is an autosomal trait in males hence very common. While it is autosomal recessive in females hence, a bald female is seen very rarely.

- **Codominance**

  When both the traits are expressed fully in heterozygous state they are called codominant. For example, a person with blood group AB shows both A and B antigens on his red blood cells. The allelic genes A and B, which are present near the tip of long arm of chromosomal 9, are therefore codominant.

- **Intermediate inheritance**
  In the heterozygous condition of an recessive trait abnormal (mutant) allele is unable to express itself. However, when in heterozygous condition if it shows intermediate expression between an abnormal homozygous and a normal homozygous then this is known as intermediate inheritance. For example in sickle cell anemia the heterozygous possesses both abnormal as well as normal haemoglobin.

Some Common Autosomal Dominant Disorders

Huntington's chorea

Incidence: 1 in 15,000 people.

Clinical features:

- The disorder of movements start appearing slowly during middle age of life (around 40 years of age). However, in 10% of cases disorder is seen before the age of 20 years (Juvenile Huntington's disease).
- Chorea is the most common movement abnormality.
- There are involuntary movements like facial grimacing, twitching of face and limbs and folding of arms and legs. After sometimes gait becomes unsteady and speech unclear.
- Intellectual functions are gradually affected (frequent loss of memory and poor concentration) which ultimately leads to dementia.

Cause of the disorder: Progressive cell death in CNS.

Genetics:

- It is an autosomal dominant disease with almost complete penetrance.
- The gene of Huntington's disease is located on the short arm of chromosome number 4.
- The gene contains abnormally large CAG repeat sequence located in 5' region. If the repeat size is more the onset of disease will be at an early age.
- Gene codes for a protein called **Huntingtin** which has been suggested that it may be responsible for cell death or apoptosis in central nervous system.

Counselling: Prenatal diagnosis is possible.

Myotonic dystrophy

Incidence: 1 in 8000 people.

Clinical features:

- Onset of disease is in adult life. Patient suffers from progressive weakness and myotonia (tonic spasm of muscle).

- There is disturbed gastrointestinal peristalsis.
- Catract and defect in cardiac conduction is also common.
- Early onset of myotonic dystrophy is also seen and may be present at birth. Baby suffers from hypotonia and respiratory distress.

Genetics:

- It is autosomal dominant disorder with **anticipation**. Anticipation is a phenomenon in which the disease occurs with increasing severity in subsequent generations and the age of onset of the disease is early as compared to the parents.
- The gene for myotonic dystrophy is located on the long arm of chromosome number 19.
- The gene contains abnormally large CTG repeat sequences at 3' region.
- In a normal person the triplet repeat size is 5 to 35. However, in affected person (with full mutation) the expanded repeat size of CTG triplet is between 50 to 2000.
- The gene is responsible for synthesis of **myotonic dystrophy protein kinase**. At present it is not known as to how this protein kinase is responsible for clinical features of myotonic dystrophy.

Counselling:

- Prenatal diagnosis is advisable.
- Regular checkup of myotonic dystrophy patients should be carried out for cardiac conduction defects.

Familial hypercholesterolaemia

Incidence: 1 in 500 people.

Clinical features:

- Because the defect is in LDL receptors there occurs the increase synthesis of endogenous cholesterol.
- Early onset of atherosclerosis (narrowing of the lumen of arteries due to deposition of fatty substances in the wall of the arteries).
- Increased level of blood cholesterol which can not be treated by dietary restriction.
- Increased risk of myocardial infarction (heart attack).
- Patient may show nodules in tendons near the knuckles.
- There may occur the subcutaneous deposition of lipid (**Xenthomata**).

Genetics:

- The disorder is autosomal dominant.
- Most of affected individuals are heterozygous. Homozygotes for high cholesterol allele are very rare. Their serum cholesterol level is highly raised and they die from heart attack by 20 years of age.
- The disease is due to mutation in the gene for LDL receptors which leads either to defective synthesis or functioning of low density lipoprotein (LDL) receptors.

Achondroplasia

Incidence: 1 in 10,000 people.

Clinical features:

- Affected person is a dwarf
- They are of normal intelligence
- They usually live a normal life and also reproduce normally.

Genetics:

- It is an autosomal dominant disorder.
- Affected individuals are usually heterozygous.
- It is a developmental disorder which is caused by the mutation in fibroblast growth factor gene leading to defective cartilage growth.
- Gene for this is situated on the short arm of chromosome number 4.

Fig. 7.5: *A group of persons affected with achondroplasia. Courtesy of "www. mun.ca".*

Neurofibromatosis

Incidence: 1 in 3000 people.

Clinical features:

- Pea sized small soft fleshy benign tumours appear on skin during late childhood.
- Small pigmented skin lesions.
- Macrocephaly (abnormal large size of head).
- Delay in physical development.
- Some may suffer from epilepsy.
- Few may develop scoliosis (lateral bending of vertebral column).

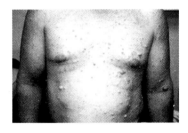

Fig. 7.6: *Neurofibromatosis. Person showing pea sized small tumours and pigmented skin lesions.*

Genetics:

- Neurofibromatosis shows autosomal dominant inheritance with almost complete penetrance and variable expression.
- Gene is present on long arm of chromosome 17 close to centromere.
- This gene encodes a protein known as neurofibromin.
- Neurofibromatosis gene acts as tumour suppressor gene. This gene plays an important role in cell growth and differentiation. The tumour development is due to loss of both alleles.

Counselling:

Though no treatment is available prenatal diagnosis can be advised.

ABO BLOOD GROUPS

There are certain constituents (proteins) found on the surface of red blood cells which determine the blood groups. There are four different blood groups i.e. A, B, AB and O. An individual may have one of four blood types (groups) depending on types of the substance present on red blood cells (A, B, A and B, neither A nor B).

Types of substance present on RBC	Blood group
A	A
B	B
A and B	AB
Nil	O

Genetics:

- Gene for ABO blood type is located near the tip of long arm of chromosome 9. This gene has more than two allelic forms.
- ABO blood groups are due to three alleles at a single locus. Thus ABO blood group is a good example of **multiple alleles**. These alleles are designated as A, B and O. An individual can possess any two of these alleles which are present on homologous chromosomes.

Genotype	Phenotype (Blood group)
AA/AO	A
BB/BO	B
AB	AB
OO	O

- Thus A and B alleles are dominant over O.
- When both A and B alleles are present together both are expressed. This phenomenon is called as **co-dominance**.

AUTOSOMAL RECESSIVE INHERITANCE

For the expression of this trait the gene should be in homozygous state (double dose). Following is the list of some common autosomal recessive disorders and traits.

Blond hair

Microphthalmia

Absence of sweat glands

Sickle cell anemia (see Ch. 9)

Phenylketonuria (see Ch. 8)
Alkaptonuria (see Ch. 8)
Microcephaly
Spinal muscular atrophy

Schizophrenia
Retinal glioma
Cystic fibrosis
Albinism (see Ch. 8)

Characteristics of autosomal recessive inheritance

As stated earlier the recessive trait is expressed only when mutant allele is present in a double dose (homozygous state).

A person having a single mutant gene (heterozygous) does not express the disorder and is perfectly healthy. An heterozygous individual for an autosomal recessive trait is called **carrier**.

Following are the features which help to determine this mode of inheritance.

- This trait is seen in same generation, among brothers and sisters siblings. It is not seen in previous (parents) or subsequent generation (offspring). In Fig. 7.7 disorder is seen only in IV generation and not in III or V generation.
- Males and females are equally affected.
- Parents of proband may be (closely related, Fig. 7.7). If the parents are first cousins the chances of manifesting recessive disorder increases many folds as compared to parents who are unrelated.

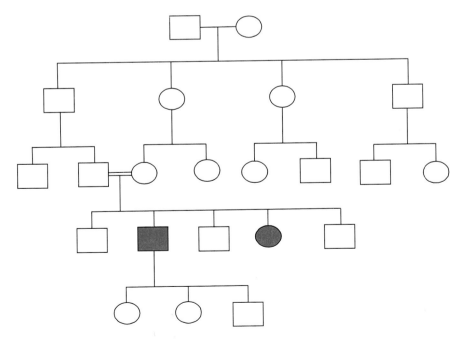

Fig. 7.7: *Pedigree of a typical autosomal recessive inheritance.*

- The genetic risk of autosomal recessive inheritance is shown as under Fig. 7.8 shows results of mating between two carriers.

The results of mating between an affected individual and a carrier shows 50% of the offspring are affected. It may be easily confused for dominant inheritance (Fig. 7.9). This kind of inheritance is called as **pseudo-dominant inheritance**.

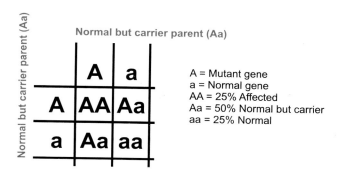

Fig. 7.8: *Mating between two carrier (Heterozygous) parents (Aa × Aa).*

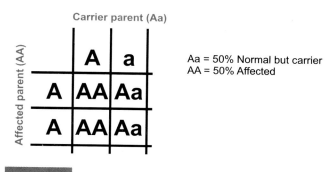

Fig. 7.9: *Mating between one carrier (Aa) and one affected (AA) parents (AA × Aa).*

Some common autosomal recessive disorders

Spinal muscular atrophy

Incidence: 1 in 10,000 people.

Clinical features:

- The characteristic of this disease is progressive weakness of muscles due to degeneration of spinal motor neurons.

- Children with severe form of spinal muscular atrophy (type I) are born with hypotonia and lack of spontaneous movement. In mild form of disease (types II and III) the onset of muscle weakness may be delayed till the age of 18 months.
- In severe form of the disease the death occurs within two years of life due to sever muscular weakness which affects swallowing and respiratory function. While in milder form of cases death occurs due to recurrent respiratory failure.

Genetics:

- It is an autosomal recessive disorder.
- The gene is located on the long arm of chromosome number 5.

Counseling:

- Prenatal diagnosis, carrier detection and therapeutic interventions are not available at present.

Cystic fibrosis (Mucoviscidosis)

Incidence: 1 in 2500 people in population. It is the most common serious disorder seen in the children of white population of Europe.

Clinical features:

- The disease is characterized by the accumulation of thick, sticky, honey like mucous secretion which leads to blockage of airways and secondary infection. This is due to the malfunction of glands of respiratory tract.
- Due to repeated infection of lung, lung tissue gets fibrosed which, leads to secondary cardiac failure (cor-pulmonale).
- The other glands affected are pancreas and the glands of gastrointestinal tract. The thick secretion leads to the blockage of the pancreatic ducts which in turn leads to reduced enzyme secretion. The chief symptoms are malnutrition resulting from incomplete digestion and absorption of fats and proteins leading to cirrhosis of liver.
- The obstruction of small intestine is common newborn due to thickened meconium.
- Cystic fibrosis in males is almost always associated with the congenital bilateral absence of vas deferens, which make them sterile.
- Death usually occurs in childhood or adolescence. The life can be prolonged up to 30 years of age with effective treatment.

Genetics:

- Cystic fibrosis shows autosomal recessive inheritance.
- The gene of C.F. is present on the long arm of chromosome number 7.
- The C.F. gene was cloned in 1989 and was named cystic fibrosis transmembrane conductance regulator (CFTR) gene.
- The CFTR protein contains 1480 amino acids which act as a chloride channel. The mutation occurs in 508th codon which results in loss of phenylalanine. The mutant

gene ultimately reduces the level of intracellular sodium chloride (which is necessary for secretion of normal mucus) which leads to the secretion of thick sticky mucus.

Counselling:

* Prenatal diagnosis should be advised to the parents of affected child.
* Gene therapy may be available in next few years.

SEX-LINKED INHERITANCE

This kind of inheritance is due to the genes located on X or Y chromosomes. This inheritance is of two different kinds.

    a. Y-linked
    b. X-linked

Y-linked inheritance

The **Y-linked** inheritances are very few. The Y-chromosome bears H-Y histocompatibility antigen genes and genes for spermatogenesis. Another trait i.e. hairy ears is also considered to be Y-linked trait.

An affected male transmits Y-linked trait to all his sons but daughters remain unaffected (as they do not contain Y chromosome). Thus in Y-linked inheritance:

* Only males are affected
* All sons of affected males are also affected
* Females never transmit the trait.

X-linked Inheritance

Usually X-linked inheritance means sex linked inheritance because Y-linked inheritance are very few. The X-linked inheritance may be either recessive or dominant.

X-linked recessive inheritance

Some of the genes on X-chromosomes are functionally similar to the genes present on the autosomes. These genes have functions other then the determination of sex e.g., gene for colour perception or gene for blood clotting. Following are few X-linked recessive disorders:

* Diabetes mellitus
* Haemophilia
* Colour blindness
* Duchenne Muscular Dystrophy

Females have two X-chromosomes while males have only one. As recessive traits only manifests when genes are in double dose (homozygous). Hence, recessive traits are very rare in females. An heterozyous female though will not manifest the trait as they have a normal allele on another homologous chromosome to compensate for recessive mutation. However, an heterozygous female will transmit the gene to next generation. Hence, heterozygous females for recessive trait are called as carriers. As the males have only one X chromosome the mutant gene will manifest the disorder even in single dose (as they do not have a normal allele to compensate for mutant gene). Therefore a male with a mutant gene on his X chromosome is called **hemizygous** for that allele. The affected male will transmit this gene to all his daughters who will become carrier and will transmit the disease to 50% of his grand sons.

Following are the characteristics of X-linked recessive inheritance

- Predominantly males are affected. (A female will be affected only when she becomes homozygous for the mutant gene i.e. when mutant genes are present in double dose. However this condition is quite rare.)
- This disorder is transmitted through unaffected carrier females to their sons.
- The affected males can not transmit the disorder to their sons as the gene is not present on Y-chromosome (Figs. 7.10 and 7.13).
- Affected males usually have normal parents as the mutant gene on X-chromosome is received through normal carrier mother (Fig. 7.13).

The genetic risk of the autosomal recessive inheritance is given below by Punnet squares (Figs. 7.11 and 7.12). If "a" is the normal allele and "A" is the mutant allele then the genotype of carrier female will be Aa. On other hand the genotype of normal male will be "ay" (as **a** is present on single X-chromosome and as there is no homologous allele on Y-chromosome hence, it is represented by Y).

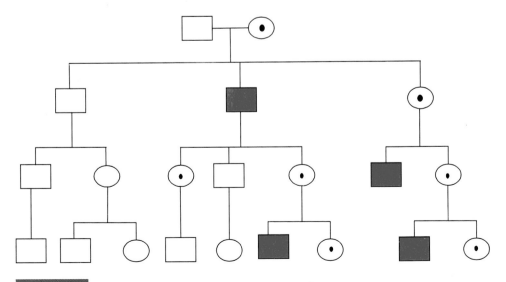

Fig. 7.10: *A pedigree of X-linked recessive inheritance.*

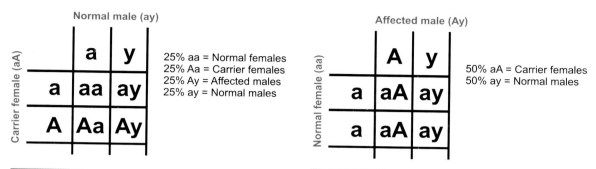

Fig. 7.11: *A mating between normal male (ay) and carrier female (aA).*

Fig. 7.12: *A mating between affected male (Ay) and normal female (aa). Thus an affected male will never transmit the disorder to his son.*

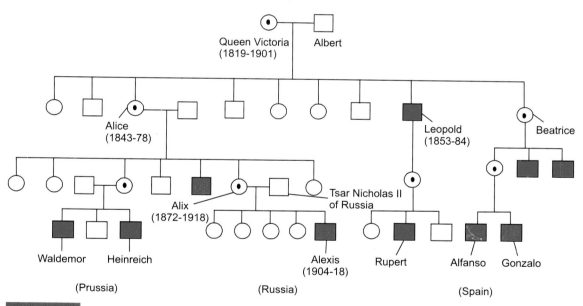

Fig. 7.13: *Pedigree chart of haemophilia among the descendents of Queen Victoria showing the spread of disease in most of the royal families of Europe through her one affected son (Leopold) and two of her daughter (Alice and Beatrice).*

Some Common X-linked Recessive *Disorders*

Duchenne muscular dystrophy

Incidence: 1 in 3500 males.

Clinical features:

- Duchenne muscular dystrophy (DMD) is the commonest and most severe form of muscular dystrophy seen in males.
- Slow and progressive muscle weakness start presenting soon after the age of 3 years.
- Severe weakness and wasting occurs in proximal muscles of lower limbs.
- Calf muscles are replaced by fat and connective tissue which leads to pseudo-hypertrophy.
- Boys can not walk by the age of 11 years and have to use a wheel chair.
- Joint contracture and respiratory failure leads to death around 18 years of age.

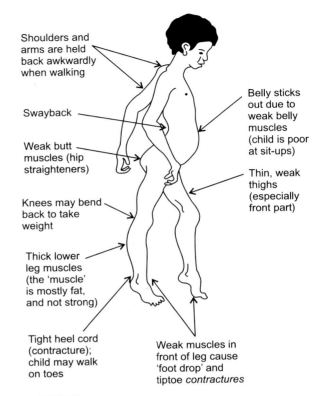

Fig. 7.14: *Duchenne muscular dystrophy. Note the sever weakness and wasting of muscles.*

Genetics:

- DMD shows X-linked recessive inheritance.
- The location of gene is on short arm of X-chromosome (Xp21).
- DMD gene encodes a protein known as dystrophin. Absence of which is responsible for muscle cell degeneration.
- There is the increase permeability of the muscle membrane which leads to the escape of muscle enzymes into blood.

Diagnosis: Increase level of serum creatine kinase (ck).

Counselling:

- Physiotherapy is beneficial.
- No treatment is available at present though the future of gene therapy seems to be promising.

Haemophilia

Haemophilia is an inherited coagulation disorder. For blood coagulation factors VIII and IX are needed which converts prothrombin to thrombin. Thrombin converts fibrinogen to fibrin which forms the structural framework of clotted blood.

Incidence:

Haemophilia are of two different kinds i.e. haemophilia A and haemophilia B. Haemophilia A (royal haemophilia) is caused by deficiency of factor VIII and has an incidence of 1 in 5000 males. Many royal families of Europe have suffered this kind of haemophilia (Fig. 7.13). Haemophilia B (Christmas disease) is caused by deficiency of factor IX and it has an incidence of 1 in 40000 males.

Clinical features:

- Prolonged bleeding occurs following trauma or surgery.
- Spontaneous bleeding may occur into muscles and joints.

Genetics:

- Haemophilia shows in an X-linked recessive inheritance.
- The genes for haemophilia A and B are located on the long arm of X chromosome, near its distal end.

Counselling:

- Plasma-derived factor VIII or IX is used as replacement therapy.
- Gene therapy may be available in near future.

X-linked dominant inheritance

This disorder is due to the presence of a mutant gene on X-chromosome. As the gene is dominant it expresses in heterozygous females as well as in males. The X-linked dominant

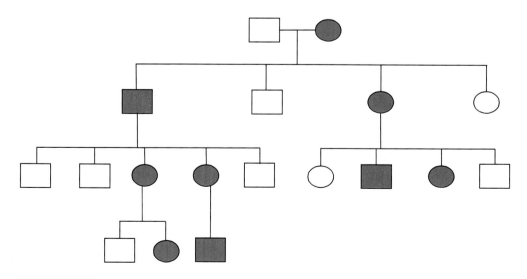

Fig. 7.15: *A pedigree of X-linked dominant inheritance.*

inheritance resembles that of an autosomal dominant inheritance but can be differentiated because of the fact that an affected male transmit this trait to all his daughters but to none of his sons. Therefore to distinguish this trait from autosomal trait one has to follow the progeny of affected male (Fig. 7.15).

Following three disorders are X-linked dominant:
- Vitamin D-resistant rickets
- Xg-blood groups
- Hypophosphatemia

MITOCHONDRIAL INHERITANCE

Mitochondrial DNA (mtDNA) is maternally inherited i.e., the mitochondria of the fertilized zygote are inherited almost exclusively from the oocyte. As the egg is the major contributor of cytoplasm to the zygote this inheritance is also known **cytoplasmic inheritance.** The mitochondrial inheritance follows a pattern as shown in Fig. 7.16.

Mitochondrial inheritance is also known as maternal inheritance because the disorder is only transmitted through the mother to all her sons and daughters. Affected males can not transmit the disease to their offspring.

Usually a human cell contains many thousand mitochondria (1,000 to 10,000). More mitochondria are found in cells where energy requirement is more i.e., brain and muscles. The mtDNA shows high mutation rate as compared to the nuclear DNA. Mitochondrial mutation may cause disease. Most of these conditions decrease the ATP generating capacity of a cell or tissue. The most common tissues to be affected are thus muscles and nervous tissues. Hence, mutation in mtDNA leads to variable clinical features i.e., hypotonia of

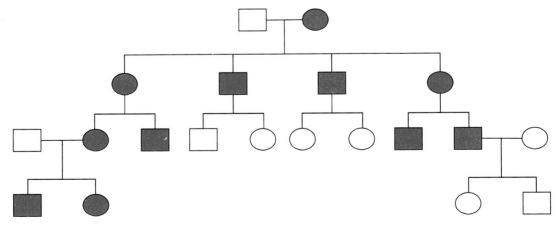

Fig. 7.16: *Pedigree of mitochondrial inheritance. Note that both males and females are affected, but disease is transmitted only through females. Affected males do not transmit the disease to their offspring.*

skeletal muscles, cardiomyopathy, neuropathy, seizures, dementia, encephalopathy, ataxia, stroke, dystonia and acidosis. Some of the mtDNA disorder are:

- Leber Hereditary Optic Neuropathy; Neurodegeneration Ataxia and Retinitis Pigmentosa (NARP)
- Mitochondrial Encephalomyopathy, Lactic Acidosis and Stroke like Episodes (MELAS)
- Myoclonic Epilepsy and Rogged Red Fiber Disease (MERRF) etc.

As there are many mitochondria in a single cell, to begin with only few mitochondria will get mutate and others will remain normal. Therefore, the expression of the disease will vary depending upon the number of mutant mitochondria in the cell. If the proportion of the mutant mitochondria is less than the disease may not even manifest in a person as large proportion of mitochondria are normal. As the proportion of mutant mitochondria increases the clinical severity of the disease also increases from "mild" to "severe". Thus when there are two populations of mitochondria within a cell i.e., normal and mutant, the condition is called as **hetroplasmy**.

POLYGENIC AND MULTIFACTORIAL INHERITANCE

There are many common traits and disorders which do not follow the pattern of simple Mendelian (single gene) inheritance. Many common traits like intelligence, blood pressure, height, weight, hair colour, eye colour and facial appearance have more complex genetic basis. If height were to be determined by a pair of genes (as in case of Mendelian inheritance) then this would result in only two different types of individuals i.e. short and tall (if suppose we represent gene for tallness as 'T' and for shortness as 't' then tall individual will be TT or Tt and short tt). However, in each family we get individuals whose height show quantitative variation from one extreme to another. All the above mentioned traits can not be clearly classified into two distinct groups but are measured quantitatively and are called **continuous traits** or **quantitative traits**.

Similarly, the following disorders also do not follow the Mendelian (monogenic) inheritance. However, these disorders can not be measured as height or blood pressure. These disorders are either present or absent. These are called threshold traits: Threshold traits are either present or absent e.g. a person is either diabetic or non-diabetic. Following are the examples of threshhold traits.

Congenital Malformation	Adult onset disease
Neural tube defects	Diabetes mellitus
Pyloric stenosis	Epilepsy
Cleft lip	Hypertension
Cleft palate	Ischemic heart disease
Heart defects	Schizophrenia, Glaucoma

The above mentioned threshold traits are considered to be determined by the action of many genes which are situated at different loci on chromosomes each of which exerts an equal additive effect. This kind of inheritance is called as **polygenic inheritance**. Here the genes do not behaves as dominant or recessive but have an additive effect on the trait.

It is also believed that these common physical traits, disorders or congenital malformations are not entirely determined by the action of many genes but are thought to result from the interaction of environmental and genetic factors. Many environmental factors like diet (in case of weight), sunlight (in case of skin colour) disease, chemicals and radiation etc. may influence the action of genes. Thus polygenic inheritance is also called as **Multifactorial inheritance**.

SUMMARY

- The inheritance of common traits or disorders follows either **monogenic** (single gene) or **polygenic** (multiple genes) pattern of inheritance.
- The monogenic or Mendelian inheritance is due to abnormal single gene which may be present on autosome (**autosomal inheritance**) or sex-chromosome (**sex-inked inheritance**).
- In case of **autosomal dominant inheritance** the gene expresses itself even in heterozygous state (single dose).
- In case of **autosomal recessive inheritance** the trait or disorder is manifested only when gene is in homozygous state (double dose).
- Following are the characteristics of **autosomal dominant** inheritance:
  - Both sexes (males and females) are equally affected. This indicates that gene is present on autosome.
  - 50% of offspring in each generation are affected.
  - Normal offspring do not transmit the disorder to next generation.
- **Pleiotrophy** - When a single gene disorder produces multiple phenotypic effect then it is called pleiotrophy.
- Following are the characteristics of **autosomal recessive** inheritance:
  - The disorder is seen in one generation only (among brothers and sisters).
  - Both sexes are equally affected.
  - Parents of affected offspring are closely related.
- Following are the characteristics of **X-linked recessive** inheritance:
  - Males are predominantly affected.
  - Unaffected carrier females transmit the disease to their sons.
  - Affected males can not transmit the disease to their sons as the gene is present on X chromosome.
- Following are the characteristics of **X-linked dominant** inheritance:
  - Disease is expressed in both males and females.
  - The inheritance pattern is similar to autosomal dominant.
  - But in this inheritance affected male transmit the disease to all his daughters but to none of his sons.

- Following are the characteristics of **mtDNA inheritance**:
    - This disorder is only transmitted by the mother to all her sons and daughters.
    - Affected males can not transmit the disease to their offspring.
- In case of **polygenic** inheritance a trait or disorder is determined by the additive effect of many genes which are situated at different loci on chromosomes.
- Polygenic traits are not entirely determined by genes but the action of genes is also affected by environmental factors. Thus polygenic inheritance is also called as **multifactorial inheritance**.

8 Biochemical Genetics

- One Gene One Enzyme
  Hypothesis

- Some Common Inborn Errors of
  Metabolism

Biochemical genetics is the combination of genetics and biochemistry and deals with the genetic control of metabolic pathways. To understand this the following facts should be noted.

- In human various metabolic processes are completed in various steps (Fig. 8.1). Each step is under the control of an enzyme. All enzymes are protein in nature and their synthesis is under the control of genes. Thus each metabolic step is under the control of one gene.

One gene one enzyme hypothesis:

G.W. Beadle and E.L. Tatum gave this hypothesis, according to which each step of metabolic process is catalysed by a specific enzyme which inturn is synthesized under the control of specific gene. However, according to the recently published draft of Human Genome Project (2001) the genetic control of metabolic process may not be so simple as stated by Beadle and Tatum. Genes function as complex network rather than single gene producing single enzyme. Hence, "one gene one enzyme" hypothesis may be modified in near future.

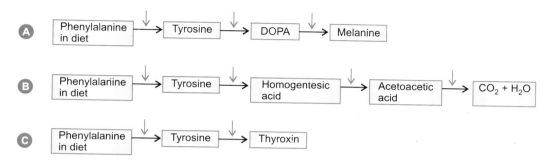

Fig. 8.1: *Biochemical pathways of phenylalanine metabolism in normal man. Phenylalanine is an essential amino acid of dietary proteins. Each step in its metabolism is controlled by a specific enzyme. In this figure phenylalanine is shown to metabolise to **A**. Melanine **B**. CO_2 and H_2O and **C**. To Thyroxin with the help of various enzymes (shown by arrows).*

- If there is a defect in enzyme, which in turn may be due to defect in gene (alteration in DNA sequence due to mutation), it will produce either the alteration in metabolic process or the process may be blocked at that particular stage.
- The error in the metabolic pathway is ultimately expressed in the form of a disease. These diseases are called as "**inborn errors of metabolism**" and were first described by A.E. Garrod in 1909.
- The mode of inheritance of inborn errors of metabolism follows the Mendelian laws of inheritance (autosomal recessive, autosomal dominant and X-linked).
- At present more than 200 inborn errors of metabolism are known. Some most common of these are listed in Table 8.1.

Some common inborn errors of metabolism

PHENYLKETONURIA

Phenylalanine is an essential amino acid which is normally converted to tyrosine with the help of enzyme **phenylalanine hydroxylase** (Fig. 8.2). Due to deficiency of this enzyme the metabolism of phenylalanine follows an alternate pathway. As a result of enzyme defect, phenylalanine instead of converting into tyrosine, is converted into phenylpyruvic acid and is excreted in the urine (Fig. 8.2).

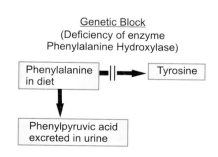

Fig. 8.2: *Absence of enzyme phenylalanine hydroxylase leads to phenylketonuria.*

Table 8.1 *Some important inborn errors of metabolism (AR=Autosomal Recessive, AD=Autosomal Dominant, XR=X-linked Recessive, Mt=Mitochondrial and MR=Mental Retardation)*

	Type of Metabolism	Mode of Inheritance	Nature of Deficient Enzyme	Clinical Features
A.	*Amino acid metabolism*			
	• Phenylketonuria	AR	Phenylalanine hydroxylase	Mental retardation, epilepsy, fair skin
	• Alkaptonuria	AR	Homogentisic acid oxidase	Arthritis
	• Oculo cutaneous Albinism	AR	Tyrosinase	Lack of pigments in the eye (result in the poor visual acuity), skin and hair
B.	*Urea cycle disorder*			
	• Hyperargininaemia	AR	Arginase	Hyperammonaemia, progressive spasticity
C.	*Carbohydrate metabolism*			
	• Galactosaemia	AR	Galactose-1-phosphate uridyl transferase	M.R., Cirrhosis, catract
	• Von Gierke's disease (Glucose storage disease)	AR	Glucose-6-phosphatase	Hypoglycaemia Hepatomegaly
D.	*Steroid metabolism*			
	• Testicular feminization	XR	Androgen receptor	External genitalia of female but internal genitalia of male
	• Congenital adrenal hyperplasia	AR	21 hydroxylase 11 B hydroxylase 3B–dehydrogenase	Salt loss, virilizaiton
E.	*Lipid metabolism*			
	• Familial hypercholester-olaemia	AD	Low density lipoprotein receptor	Early coronary artery disease
F.	*Lysosomal storage disease*			
	• Hurler's syndrome	AR	α-l, iduronidase	M.R., hepatospleen-omegaly, Corneal,

				clouding, skeletal abnormalities
	• Hunter's syndrome	XR	Iduronate sulphate sulphatase	M.R., Hepatosplenomegaly, skeletal abnormalities
G.	*Lipid storage diseases* • Tay-Sachs disease	AR	Hexosaminidase - A	Deafness, blindness, cherry red spot
	• Gaucher's disease	AR	Glucosylceramide β-glucosidase	Joint and limb pains, splenomegaly
H.	*Porphyrin metabolism* • Acute intermittent porphyria	AD	Uroporphyrinogen I synthetase	Abdominal pain, CNS effects
I.	*Copper metabolism* • Wilson disease	AR	ATPase membrane copper transport protein	Spasticity, rigidity, dysphagia, cirrhosis
J.	*Mitochondrial diseases* MELAS	Mt	Mutation in leucine tRNA	Encephalomyopathy Lactic acidosis
	MERRF	Mt	Mutation in lysine tRNA	Myopathy, optic atrophy Seizures, dementia
	Leber hereditary optic neuropathy	Mt	Mutation in ND4 gene	Retinal degeneration

Incidence: 1 in 10,000 people.

Clinical features:

- Child suffers from mental retardation and epilepsy. Child born with phenylketonuria is normal at birth, but subsequently as it receives phenylalanine in diet it gets converted into phenylpyruvic acid. This toxic metabolite of phenylalanine is responsible for epilepsy and mental retardation as seen in children.
- Enzyme block leads to deficiency of tyrosine which in turn leads to reduction in melanin formation.
- Blond hair, blue eyes and lack of pigment in substantia nigra.

Diagnosis:

- The diagnosis of phenylketonuria can be made by detecting the presence of phenylpyruvic acid in the urine (ferric chloride test).
- By estimating the elevated level of phenylalanine in blood by direct fluorometric essays.

Genetics:

- Phenylketonuria results due to mutation of gene responsible for coding phenylalanine hydroxylase.
- The mode of inheritance of disease is autosomal recessive.

Counseling:

- No treatment is available except restricting the amount of phenylalanine in diet.
- Early diagnosis will prevent conditions like mental retardation and epilepsy.

ALBINISM

Albinism is also referred as **oculocutaneous** albinism. This disease is due to deficiency of enzyme **tyrosinase** which converts the DOPA into melanine pigment (Fig. 8.3).

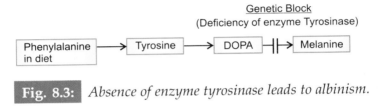

Fig. 8.3: *Absence of enzyme tyrosinase leads to albinism.*

Clinical features:

- Affected person shows the lack of pigment in skin, hair, iris and ocular fundus.
- They also suffer from poor visual acuity and nystagmus (uncontrolled pendular eye movement).

Genetics:

- The albinism is due to mutation in the gene responsible for coding enzyme tyrosinase. Because of this DOPA is not converted to melanine (Fig. 8.3).
- This gene is located on long arm of chromosome 11. This kind of albinism is known as oculocutaneous albinism type I.
- In some families albinism is due to mutation of P gene located on long arm of chromosome 15. This kind of albinism is called oculocutaneous albinism type II.
- The mode of inheritance is autosomal recessive.

GALACTOSAEMIA

Glactosaemia is an inborn error of carbohydrate metabolism where patient is unable to metabolise monosaccharide sugar galactose. This is due to the deficiency of enzyme **galactose-1-phosphate uridyl transferase**.

Clinical feature:

- Infants in their second week of life suffer from vomiting, lethargy, failure to thrive and jaundice.
- If child remains untreated may develop mental retardation, cataracts and cirrhosis of liver.

Diagnosis:

Detection of reducing substance in urine with specific testing for galactose.

Genetics:

- This is an autosomal recessive inborn error of metabolism.
- This is due to mutation of gene responsible for coding enzyme galactose-1-phosphate uridyl transferase.

Counseling:

- Early diagnosis and treatment are necessary to prevent complications.
- Affected infant should be fed with the milk substitute which should not contain galactose and lactose. (The removal of lactose from diet is also necessary as lactose is broken down into galactose.)

FAMILIAL HYPERCHOLESTEROLAEMIA

See chapter 7.

HURLER'S SYNDROME

Hurler's syndrome is a kind of **mucopolysaccharidoses** (MPS I) which is due to deficiency of a lysosomal enzyme "**α-L-iduronidase**" which is involved in the degradation of complex macromolecules. Absence of the enzyme results in the accumulation of this kind of macromolecules i.e. sulphated polysaccharides (**glycosaminoglycans**) which leads to the disorder.

Clinical features:

- During first year of life affected infants show retarded growth, corneal clouding and abnormal curve in lower spine.
- During second year of life they develop coarse facial features, hepatosplenomegaly, joint stiffness and vertebral changes. They develop loss of hearing.
- Mental retardation becomes apparent in early childhood.
- They usually die in their mid teens due to cardiac failure and respiratory infections.

Diagnosis:

- There is increases in urinary excertion of dermatan and heparan sulphate.
- The level of α-L-iduronidase enzyme is reduced.

Genetics:
- It is an autosomal recessive disorder.
- This is due to mutation of gene which codes for lysosomal hydrolytic enzyme α-L-iduronidase.

Counseling:
- Bone marrow transplantation may be advised.

WILSON DISEASE

Wilson disease is the disorder of copper metabolism. There is deficiency of "ATPase membrane copper transport protein" which is required to transfer copper from liver cells to the biliary passage. This leads to the abnormally high level of copper in the liver.

Clinical features:
- Abnormal neurological findings (difficulty in speech and swallowing) and fits. These symptomps first appear in childhood or in early teens.
- Psychiatric disturbances.
- Spasticity and rigidity of muscles.

Diagnosis:
- Decrease serum concentration of "ceruloplasmin" (a copper transport protein).
- Copper loading tests.

Genetics:
- It is an autosomal recessive disease. The inheritance is matrilineal i.e., the disease is transmitted to offspring only through mother. Affected males do not transmit the disease to their offspring.

Treatment:
- Abnormal neurological findings improve when patient is treated by chelating agents like D-penicillamine and trientine.

MERRF (Myoclonic Epilepsy and Ragged Red Fiber Disease)

In this disease there is abnormal deposit of mitochondria in the skeletal muscles termed as "ragged red". These mitochondria take red staining when muscle is stained with "Gomori-trichrome".

Clinical features:
- Progressive myoclonic epilepsy, myopathy.
- Dementia, optic atrophy.

Diagnosis:

* Abnormal EEG.

Genetics:

* Mutation in the lysine t-RNA.

MELAS (Mitochondrial Encephalomyopathy, Lactice Acidosis and Stroke like episodes)

Clinical features:

* Stroke like episodes associated with vomiting, headache, visual disturbances.
* Type II diabetes.
* Loss of hearing.

Genetics:

* Mutation in gene for leucine tRNA.

LHON (Leber Hereditary Optic Neuropathy)

Clinical features:

* Loss of central visual acuity without pain in persons between 12 to 30 years of age.

Genetics:

* Point mutation in ND4 gene at 11,778 position.

SUMMARY

* **"One gene one enzyme"** hypothesis given by Beadle and Tatum, states that:
    * Metabolic process occur in various steps.
    * Each step is under the control of an enzyme.
    * Each enzyme is coded by one gene.
* If there is mutation of gene then that specific enzyme will not be available. This will cause **inborn error of metabolism** which is due to
    * accumulation of intermediate metabolites.
    * deficiency of terminal end product.
* Inborn error of metabolism follows the Mendelian laws of inheritance i.e. A.D./A.R. or X-linked.
* Mitochondrial DNA abnormalities follow maternal inheritance.
* Many of these disorders can be screened/diagnosed and treated.
* At present more than 200 inborn errors of metabolism are known.

9 Haemoglobin Disorders

- Haemoglobin
- Disorders of Haemoglobin
- Sickle-cell Disease
- Thalassaemia

HAEMOGLOBIN

Haemoglobin is an oxygen carrying protein in red blood cells. The molecules of haemoglobin have complex, convoluted three dimensional structure. It's molecular weight is 64,000 daltons. The haemoglobin molecule has two different components i.e. the "haem" and "globin". Haem part is responsible for transport of oxygen while globin is made up of four polypeptide chains. These four polypeptide chains are arranged in two pairs i.e. two chains are of one type and other two are of different type. Each globin chain has its own iron containing haem group.

In human many types of normal haemoglobin are found in adults and during various stages of development (Table 9.1 and Fig. 9.1). The variation in haemoglobin is due to variation in their globin chains. In adult type of haemoglobin (HbA) there are two α and two β polypeptide chains ($\alpha_2\beta_2$). Similarly, in fetus (HbF) the haemoglobin has two α and two γ polypeptide chains ($\alpha_2\gamma_2$). The α globin chain contains 141 amino acids and β chain has 146 amino acids. Though γ polypeptide chain resembles to β chain but differs from it by 39 amino acids. The other globin chains like δ, ϵ (epsilon) and ζ (zeta) that are present in various forms of haemoglobins are also more like β chains.

Table 9.1 *Types of human haemoglobin*

Developmental stage	Haemoglobin	Structure	% in normal adult
Embryonic	Gower I Gower II	$\zeta_2\varepsilon_2$ $\alpha_2\varepsilon_2$	Nil Nil
Fetal	HbF	$\alpha_2\gamma_2$	Less than 1
Adult	HbA HbA2	$\alpha_2\beta_2$ $\alpha_2\delta_2$	98 2

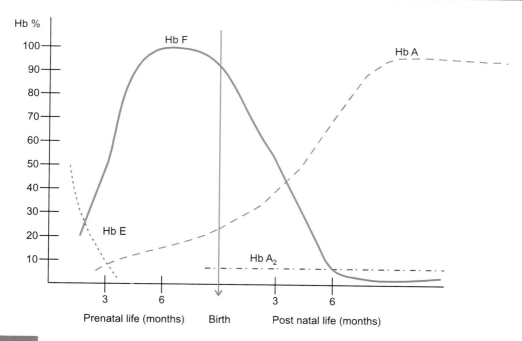

Fig. 9.1: *Various haemoglobins during prenatal and post natal life. The embryonic haemoglobin (Hb E) is present only during first three months of prenatal life. The concentration of Hb F rises to maximum soon after 3rd month of foetal life while the concentration of adult Hb reaches to maximum 6 month after birth.*

Genetics of Haemoglobin synthesis

As the globin part of haemoglobin is a protein it is coded by gene. As there are many types of polypeptide chains (α, β, ε, δ, γ, and ζ) in globin, it is expected that each type of chain must be coded by a specific gene. The α chain is coded by "α-globin structural gene" which is located in the short arm of chromosome 16. Similarly, β chain is coded by "β-globin structural gene" located on short arm of chromosome 11. The other polypeptide chains like ε, γ and δ are coded by their respective structural genes which are also situated on short arm of chromosome 11 to the 5' side of β gene (Fig. 9.2). Similarly, ζ (zeta) gene is situated on the short arm of chromosome 16 to the 5' side of α gene (Fig. 9.2). The expression of these different kinds of globin genes varies in different developmental period. The Gower I and Gower II type of Hb are produced during embryonic period by the expression of α, ζ and ε genes (Fig. 9.1). During fetal period ζ and ε genes are switched off and γ gene is switched on. However, at the end of foetal period expression of γ gene is replaced by the expression of β gene. Thus we see that a gene is active almost throughout the developmental period while γ gene remains active only during fetal period. During the postnatal life α and β genes remain active to synthesize adult haemoglobin ($\alpha_2\beta_2$).

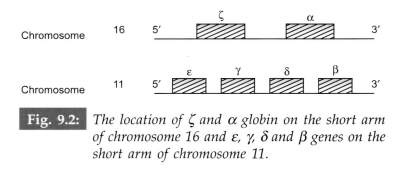

Fig. 9.2: *The location of ζ and α globin on the short arm of chromosome 16 and ε, γ, δ and β genes on the short arm of chromosome 11.*

DISORDERS OF HAEMOGLOBIN

Any change in the structure of haemoglobin molecule will produce abnormal haemoglobin that may or may not interfere with its oxygen carrying capacity. The disorders of haemoglobin are also referred as **haemoglobinopathies**. There are two different types of haemoglobinopatheies.

- Haemoglobinopathy due to change in the structure of haemoglobin chain (e.g. Sickle cell diseases).
- Haemoglobinopathy due to disorder of synthesis of globin chain (e.g. Thalassaemias).

I. *Disorders of haemoglobin due to change in the structure of globin chain.*
   The change in the structure of haemoglobin chain results in the formation of various kinds of haemoglobins. Some of these are associated with disease but many are harmless. The change in the structure of globin chain occurs due to various type of mutation in genes which inturn produce various types of haemoglobin (Table 9.2).

Table 9.2 *Disorders of human haemoglobin due to structural variation in globin chain.*

Type of Haemoglobin	Type of mutation	Chain/alteration	Effect of mutation
HbS	Point	β/6 glu to val	Sickling of RBC, haemolytic anemia
HbC	Point	β/6 glu to lys	Sickling of RBC, haemolytic anemia
HbE	Point	β/26 glu to lys	Sickling of RBC, haemolytic anemia
Hb Gun Hill	Deletion	β/92-96	unstable haemoglobin
Hereditary persistence of fetal haemoglobin	Deletion/point mutation in γ gene	Deletion of DNA sequence responsible for γ-β switch/γ chain	Continued synthesis of γ chain in adults/no clinical symptoms
Hb Grady	Insertion	α/116-118 duplication	Unstable Hb
Hb tak	Frameshift	β/11 residues are added	Unstable Hb
Hb constant spring	Chain termination	β/point mutation in terminal codon	Haemolytic anemia
Hb lepore/Anti-lepore	Fusion chain	δ-β chain fusion in lepore	–
		β-δ chain fusion in anti-lepore.	

SICKLE-CELL DISEASE

It is the most common haemoglobinopathy. In this heritable disease the main feature is of sickling of RBCs which ultimately leads to haemolytic anemia. The haemoglobin of sickle cell anemia patients (HbS) is different from the normal haemoglobin of adults (HbA).

Genetics:

* Sickle-cell disease shows autosomal recessive inheritance (affected person is homozygous for mutant gene).
* It is due to the mutation in gene responsible for coding β polypeptide chain.
* β polypeptide chain is 146 amino acid long. The 6th amino acid from the amino end of the molecule is **glutamic acid** which after mutation changes to **valine**. This is due

to the alteration in the second base pair of the triplet coding for glutamic acid in DNA sequence (i.e. from T/A pair to A/T pair) (Fig. 9.3). In the mRNA strand the code for glutamic acid (GAG) will thus change for valine (GUG). This small change (point mutation) puts one wrong amino acid in polypeptide chain that changes the properties of haemoglobin molecule. This causes various abnormalities throughout the body (see clinical features).

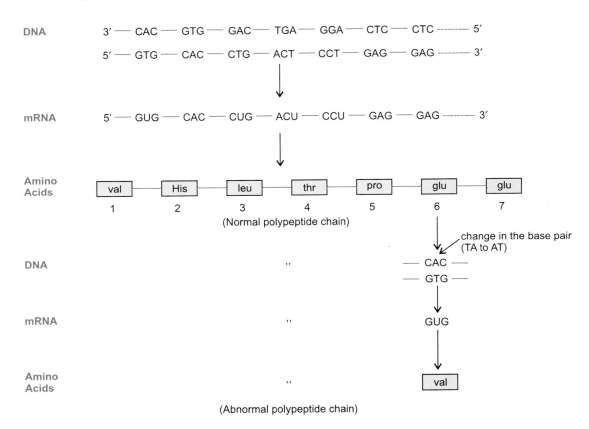

Fig. 9.3: *β-polypeptide chain showing alteration in the second base pair of 6th amino acid, which results into change of amino acid (from glutamic acid to valine).*

Why RBCs show sickling ?

The haemoglobin of sickle-cell anemia (HbS) is an abnormal haemoglobin. It is less soluble as compared to normal haemoglobin (HbA) and gets crystallized very easily specially under deoxygenated conditions. The crystallization of HbS causes the sickle shaped deformation in the shape of RBCs.

What are the effects of sickling of RBCs ?

The deformation in shape of RBCs leads to:

a. *Anemia* - This is because the sickle shaped RBCs are less stable and are destroyed rapidly. These cell have shorter life span in circulation as compared to normal red blood cells.

b. *Obstruction of small arteries* - The abnormal red blood cells tend to cluster or clump and thus obstruct the small arteries which inturn causes thrombosis, ischaemia and infarction.

Clinical features:

A. *Due to destruction of sickle shaped RBCs in spleen:*
   - *Splenomegaly* or enlargement of spleen is because it is over loaded with the task of destruction of sickle shaped RBCs (Fig. 9.4).

B. *Due to anemia:*
   As the oxygen carrying capacity of blood gets reduced it shows following effects.
   - Weakness and lassitude is due to non availability of required oxygen to body tissues.

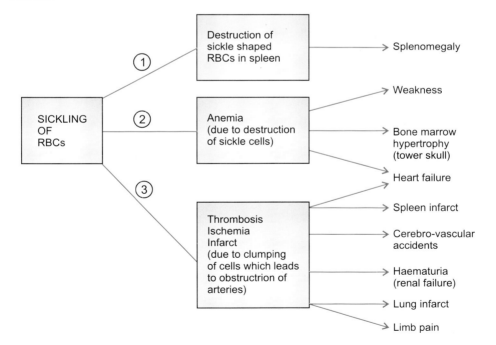

Fig. 9.4: *Sickling of RBCs in sickle cell anemia leads to arious effects (pleiotrophic) on the body due to haemolytic anemia and clumping of red blood cells.*

- Abnormal skull radiograph is due to the compensatory enlargement of bone marrow which tend to produce more and more red blood cells to cope up with anemia. Bone marrow hypertrophy in skull produces tower shaped skull.
- Failure of heart is due to over activity of heart because of anemia.

C. *Due to obstruction of small arteries*:

The thrombosis may lead to ischemia and infarction of various important organs like spleen, heart (myocardial infarct), brain (cerebrovascular accidents), gut (abdominal pain), limbs (limb pain) and kidney (haematuria) etc.

Counselling:

As compared to normal population, people suffering from sickle-cell disease die early because of anemia and complications. Life expectancy can be improved by preventing and treating the complications.

Sickle-cell trait

The sickle-cell disease is due to autosomal recessive inheritance (i.e. a person is homozygous for mutant gene). However, when a person is heterozygous (only one gene of a pair is mutant and other is normal) he is considered to be as carrier. This condition is sometimes regarded as **sickle-cell trait**. A carrier of sickle-cell disease is usually healthy because a single normal gene produces sufficient 'β' globin chain. However, they are at risk during hypoxia (specially when they go to high altitude) and following heavy exercise.

Pleiotrophic effects of a gene

Pleiotrophy refers to the fact that genes can have effect on many traits or may present with several clinical features. For example though the sickle-cell disease is due to mutation of a single gene but it has wide spread effects on various systems of the body (Fig. 9.4). The other example of pleiotrophy is **tuberous sclerosis** which is an autosomal dominant disorder. Here the affected person presents with several unrelated features like learning difficulties, epilepsy and facial rash.

Beneficial effects of sickle-cell mutation

Though mutation causes sickle cell disease but it also has one beneficial effect. In various parts of Africa the frequency of sickle-cell anemia concides with the distribution of malaria. The people suffering from sickle-cell disease are saved from malaria, because the carriers of sickle-cell allele have an enhanced resistance to falciparum malaria. This is due to the fact that malaria parasites can not infect the sickled shaped red blood cells as readily as the normal red cells. Even infected, the abnormal haemoglobin tend to sickle rapidly thus leading to early destruction of red cells alongwith parasites. Similar effect is also observed between malaria and thalassaemia (see below).

II. *Haemoglobinopathy due to disorder of synthesis of globin chain.*

THALASSAEMIAS

Thalassaemias are inherited disorders of haemoglobin which are characterised by haemolytic anemia. In thalassaemia though the globin chain is normal but it is synthesized in reduced amount. The thalassaemias are classified as:

- α Thalassaemia
- β Thalassaemia
- δβ Thalassaemia
- γδβ Thalassaemia

α-Thalassaemia

Alpha-thalassaemia is due to the reduction in synthesis of α-globin chains. As the a chain is present in fetal ($\alpha_2\gamma_2$) and adult haemoglobins ($\alpha_2\beta_2$) it affects both kind of haemoglobins. In the postnatal life as the production of β-chain is normal, there will be excess of β chains as compared to α chains. Because of this many of Hb molecules instead of having two α and β chains ($\alpha_2\beta_2$) will have all four β chains. This kind of haemoglobin molecule will have reduced affinity for oxygen.

Genetics:

- Alpha-thalassaemia is due to deletion of α gene responsible for synthesis of α-globin chain.
- There are two α genes present on short arm of each chromosome 16. Thus there are four α genes in each normal individual (Fig. 9.5).
- The deletion of one, two, three or all four α-globin genes may take place during meiosis as a result of unequal crossing over.
- The severity of α-thalassaemia is in proportion to the number of gene deleted. If all four genes are deleted the condition is called **hydrops fetalis** (see below). The death of fetus will occur in uterus thus the condition is not seen in new born or adults.

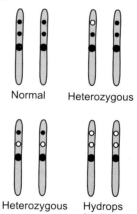

Normal   Heterozygous

Heterozygous   Hydrops fetalis

Fig. 9.5: *Normally there are two α genes present on the short arm of each chromosome 16. The severity of α-thalassaemia is in proportion to the number of α genes deleted. If only one gene is deleted it will be the milder form of α-thalassaemia.*

Clinical features:

- As β-globin chains are in excess the haemoglobin molecules with all four β-globin chains are formed. This kind of haemoglobin is unstable and precipitates easily resulting in haemolysis of the red blood cells. Thus patient suffers from anemia.
- Haemoglobin molecules with four β chains release oxygen slowly in peripheral tissue which is an another cause of anemia in the patients suffering from α-thalassaemia.

Hydrops fetalis

This is a severe form of α thalassaemia. Hydrops fetalis is due to deletion of all four genes coding for a globin (Fig. 9.5) so no α globin chains are produced. In absence of α globin chain the haemoglobin molecule of fetus is formed by four γ globin chains. This condition leads to severe anemia in fetus and results in intrauterine death.

β-Thalassaemia

Similar to a thalassaemia, there is underproduction of β-globin chain of haemoglobin in β-thalassaemia. As the β-globin chain is present only in adult haemoglobin ($\alpha_2\beta_2$), β thalassaemia affects only adult haemoglobin (HbA).

Genetics:

- Gene for β-globin chain is located on short arm of chromosome 11.
- There is only one gene on each chromosome 11, thus there are in total two genes for production of β-globin chain.
- β-thalassaemia may be due either to deletion or mutation of β-gene.
- Various types of mutations are observed in β-thalassaemia (i.e. point mutation; insertions or deletions of one or more bases). These mutations may occur within the coding or non-coding portion of β-globin gene.
- Homozygous of β-thalassaemia have severe transfusion dependent anemia. However, heterozygous suffers from milder anemia. Homozygous condition (where mutation is seen in both the genes) is sometimes referred as **thalassaemia major** or **Cooley's anemia.** The hetrozygous condition is referred as **thalassaemia minor**.

Normal   Heterozygous   Homozygous
(Thalassaemia   (Thalassaemia
Minor)   Major)

Fig. 9.6: *Gene for β chain is present on the short arm of chromosome 11. β thalassemia may be due to either deletion or mutation of β gene. In homozygous condition (absence of gene on both the chromosome 11) β chains are not produced at all.*

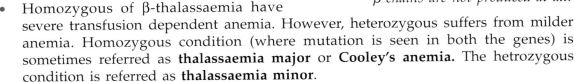

- There is mild compensatory increase in HbF ($\alpha_2\gamma_2$) in persons suffering from thalassaemia major. This is due to the prodution of γ-globin chains in postnatal life.

Clinical features:

- Heterozygous persons for β-thalassaemia (thalassaemia minor) suffer from mild anemia.
- Homozygous persons for β-thalassaemia (thalassaemia major) suffer from severe anemia. They need frequent blood transfusions.
- The severe anemia becomes evident right from first year of life and most of them survive till early twenties. Death usually occurs due to complications as a result of iron overload from repeated blood transfusion.
- Prolonged anemia leads to compensatory hypertrophy of bone marrow which results in unusual shape of face and skull.

Counselling:

- High risk group should be screened for carrier detection.
- Prenatal diagnosis of thalassaemia major can be done by fetal blood.
- Long term survival can be achieved by regular blood transfusion and by treating the complication of iron overloading.
- In absence of β-globin chain production, drugs which can promote γ globin synthesis should be prescribed. The increase production of γ-globin chain will produce HbF ($\alpha_2\gamma_2$) and can compensate for the deficient β-globin chain production.

$\delta\beta$ Thalassaemia

- This kind of anemia is due to deletion in δ and β globin structural genes. It is an extensive deletion involving the region of both δ and β genes on chromosome 11 (Fig. 9.2).
- There is under production of both δ and β-globin chains in persons who are heterozygous for $\delta\beta$ thalassaemia. However, there is no production of δ or β globin chains in homozygous person.
- Persons suffering from $\delta\beta$ thalassaemia are not severely anemic. This is due to the fact that there is persistence of production of γ-globin chain in postnatal period which results in increased level of HbF ($\alpha2\gamma2$).

SUMMARY

- Globin molecule of haemoglobin is made up of four **polypeptide chains** which are arranged in two pairs. Out of four chains two chains are of one type and remaining two of other type.
- There are many types of polypeptide chains (α, β, γ, δ, ϵ and ζ) which are coded by specific genes.

- These various types of polypeptide chains form various kinds of normal haemoglobin during embryonic, fetal and adult life. For example during embryonic period haemoglobin is made up of $\gamma_2\varepsilon_2$; during fetal period it is $\alpha_2\gamma_2$ and in adult it is $\alpha_2\beta_2$.
- Disorders of haemoglobin are referred as **haemoglobinopathies** which are either due to change in the structure of haemoglobin molecule **(sickle cell anemia)** or because of disorder of synthesis of the chain **(thalassaemia)**.
- Sickle-cell disease is due to sickling of RBCs which leads to haemolytic anemia.
- Sickling of RBCs is due to formation of abnormal haemoglobin (HbS). This abnormality is due to mutation in gene responsible for coding β polypeptide chain.
- The mode of inheritance of this disease is autosomal recessive (person is homozygous for mutant gene).
- When a person is heterozygous (only one gene of a pair is mutant and other is normal) then he is considered as carrier of disease. This condition is regarded as "**sickle cell trait**".
- **Thalassaemias** are also characterised by haemolytic anemia. Here the globin chain is normal but synthesized in reduced amount.
- Depending upon which globin chain is synthesized in reduced amount thalassaemias are classified as α, β, $\delta\ \beta$ and $\gamma\delta\beta$ thalassaemias.
- In **a thalassaemia** there occurs deletion of α gene(s) responsible for synthesis of α globin chain.
- The severity of α-thalassaemia is in proportion to number of gene deleted. There are in total $\alpha 4$ genes i.e. two on short arm of each chromosome 16.
- When all four genes are deleted the condition is called as "**hydrops fetalis**".
- β-thalassaemia is due to deletion or mutation of β-gene present on chromosome 11.
- Heterozygous persons suffer from mild anemia **(thalassaemia minor)** while homozygous persons suffer from severe anemia **(thalassaemia major or Cooley's anemia)**.

10 Immunogenetics

- Immunity
- Structure of Antibody
- Diversity of Antibody
- Immunodeficiency Diseases
- Transplantation of Tissues

IMMUNITY

What is immunity ?

We human beings are surrounded by many pathogens (viruses, bacteria, parasites etc.). Which may invade and damage our tissues and organs. But our body has an unique ability to resist the infection of microorganism. This ability is called **immunity**. The system which recognizes and destroys viruses, bacteria, cancerous cells and toxins is known as **immune system**. Even foreign tissues from other human beings or animals are treated in similar way. However, the immune system has the ability to recognize our own normal tissues and refrain from attacking them.

What is the mechanism of immunity ?

The immunity is mediated through a kind of white blood cells called as **lymphocytes.** These lymphocytes are assisted by another blood cells called **macrophages**. Lymphocytes are formed in bone marrow by **stem cells**. Once formed, these lymphocytes are differentiated in two different kinds i.e. **T** and **B** lymphocytes. The T lymphocytes are differentiated in thymus hence, also called as thymus-dependent cells. The B lymphocytes probably undergo differentiation in bone marrow hence, sometimes called as bone marrow derived cells. Most of B cells are stored in lymphoid organs of body (lymph nodes, spleen, tonsil, peyer's patches etc.) while most of T cells are always circulating in blood stream.

The microorganisms can invade our body through various body openings or wounds, thus they may invade blood or lymphatic system. The immune system monitors all foreign invaders and prepares itself to resist the invasion. The resistance to invasion is achieved in two different ways i.e. there are two different kinds of immunity.

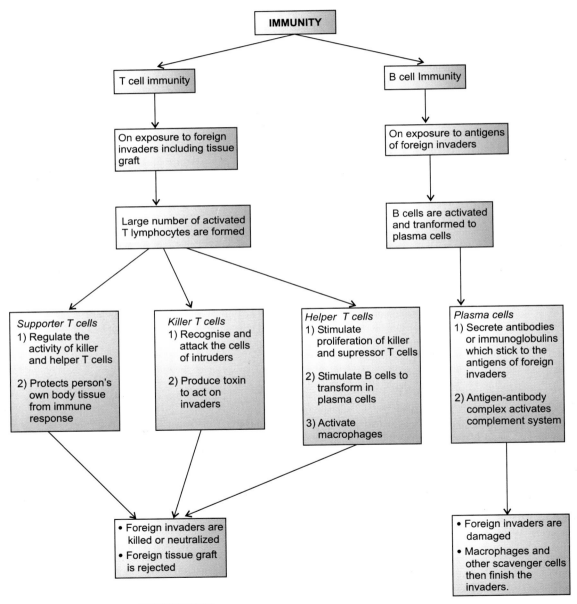

Fig. 10.1: *Basic mechanism of immune system.*

a. *T-cell immunity or cell mediated immunity.*
    This type of immunity is achieved through the activation of large number of lymphocytes. These lymphocytes are specifically designed to destroy the particular foreign invaders. There are many types of T cells (e.g. killer T cells, suppressor T cells and helper T cells) serving different functions (Fig. 10.1).
b. *B-cell immunity or humoral immunity.*
    In this type of immunity B-lymphocytes are transformed to plasma cells. These plasma cells produce antibodies or immunoglobulins which are capable of attacking invading organisms (Fig. 10.1).

Basic concepts of immunity

Antibody

An antibody (or immunoglobulin) is a protein synthesized by an animal in response to the presence of a foreign substance. The antibody has specific affinity for the foreign material which was responsible for its production. Antibodies are produced by plasma cells which are derived from B-lymphocytes. An active plasma cell produces and secretes about 2000 identical antibody molecules every second, and secretion occurs for about 4 to 5 days, until the plasma cell dies.

Antigen

Antigen is an immunity stimulating substance (a foreign macromolecule) which is capable of eliciting antibody formation. Many substances are antigenic in nature (anything which is as big or bigger than a protein molecule may act as antigenic).

Why an antigen elicits immune response?

There are identifiable features on the surface of antigens (these are large molecules on the surface of viruses, bacteria and cells of higher organisms) which are called **antigenic determinant (epitope)**. A large molecule or cell may have hundreds of different antigenic determinants. A material becomes antigenic for a person if there is presence of atleast one epitope that is recognised as foreign because it is different from the substances present in the body of that individual. A typical antigen has many different antigenic determinant and therefore elicit the production of many different antibodies. Each type of antibody is produced in response to one type of antigenic determinant of a antigen.

An antigenic determinant is recognized by B or T cell. Each B cell or T cell is capable to recognize only one antigenic determinant. Both the cells (T and B) have receptors on their surface which exactly matches with the antigenic determinant on the surface of antigen (like lock and key). Once a B cell combines with a specific determinant, it gets stimulated to undergo mitosis. The cells produced from these cell divisions are of same genetic constitution and constitute a **clone**. From this clone many cells differentiate to become plasma cells and begin to secrete antibodies. The B cell of a particular clone are capable of secreting only one kind of antibody, which is identical to antigen receptor on

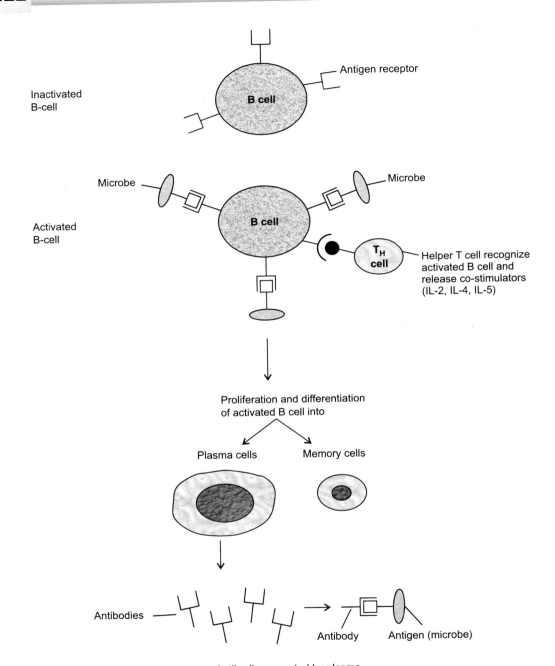

Fig. 10.2: *The activation of B cells by the antigens present on microbes to and subsequent formation of antibodies and antigen-antibody complex.*

B cells that first responded to the antigen. These antibodies then combine with specific antigens to form **antigen-antibody complex** (Fig. 10.2).

What is complement activation?

Once the antigen-antibody complex is formed it leads to "complement activation". Complement is about 20 plasma proteins, which are sequentially activated after formation of antigen-antibody complex. Some plasma proteins of the complement attack on the microorganism (present in the antigen antibody complex) and produce defect in its cell membrane. This leads to the lyses of the microorganism which is later removed by phagocytes.

Complement may also act on microorganism by activating mast cells and macrophages, which leads to the local inflammatory response.

How a body responds to thousands of antigenic substances?

It is expected that there should be thousands of different kinds of receptors on T and B cells which can recognise such a large numbers of antigenic determinants (epitopes) on antigens. In fact the above expectation is true. There is a large diversity of antigen receptors. Similarly, as there are millions of antigens receptors there should be millions of different kinds of antibodies. Antibodies are proteins and their synthesis is under the control of genes. Now a big question comes to our mind as how could thousands to million of different antigen receptors and antibodies possibly be generated specially when human cells contains only about 35,000 genes (as per the first draft of Human Genome Project, 2001).

The aim of present chapter is to answer this puzzle. To understand the diversity of antibodies we should first understand the structure of antibody (immunoglobulin).

STRUCTURE OF ANTIBODY (IMMUNOGLOBULIN)

* The immunoglobulins are glycoprotein in nature.
* Most of the antibodies contain four polypeptide chains.
* Two of these chains are long chains (each consists of about 450 amino acids) and are called heavy (H) polypeptide chains. These two chains are identical to each other. Short carbohydrate chains are attached to each heavy chain (Fig. 10.3).
* Two other chains are called **light (L)** chains or short polypeptide chains. They are also identical to each other and consist of about 220 amino acids.
* A disulfide bond holds each light chain to heavy chain.
* Two heavy chains are attached to each other in their middle portion with the help of disulfide bond. The region where two heavy chains are connected with each other is flexible and is called hinge region. Because of this flexibility an antibody can assume T or Y shape.
* Each heavy and light chain can be divided into two distinct regions. The tips of H and L chains consist of **variable (V) region** while the remaining region is called as **constant (C) region**.

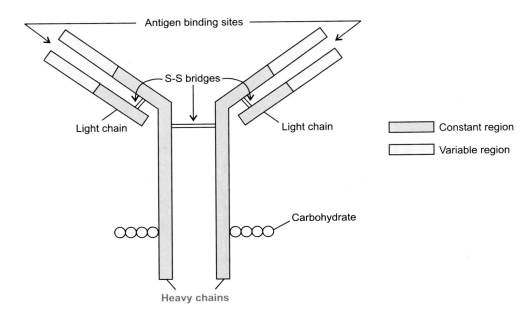

Fig. 10.3: *Diagramatic representation of IgG antibody molecule. Molecule consists of two heavy and two light polypeptide chains which are held together by S-S bridges. Each chain consist of regions with variable amino acid sequence.*

- The variable (V) region is antigen binding site. The antigen binding site of an antibody is a short of reflection of an epitope on an antigen. The variable region is different for each kind of antibody. This part recognizes and attaches to a particular antigen. Most antibodies have two antigen binding sites.
- The constant (C) region of H and L chains is nearly the same in all antibodies of same class.
- There are five different classes of heavy chains i.e. γ, μ, α, δ and ε. Based on the chemical structure of the above five heavy chains five different classes of immunoglobulins (antibodies) are designated respectively as IgG, IgA, IgM, IgD and IgE. The characteristics and function of various classes of immunoglobulins are given in Table 10.1.
- L chains are of two types only i.e. κ (Kappa) or λ (lambda).
- Thus molecular formula of IgG is $\gamma_2 \lambda_2$ or $\gamma_2 \kappa_2$.

In an normal individual there are about one million antibodies that differ in their antigen-binding specificity. This indicates that the variable region of immunoglobulin molecule may show innumerable sequences of amino acids.

Table 10.1 *Detail information about various immunoglobulins.*

Name	Molecular formula	Percentage of antibody and serum concentration (mg/ml.)	Function of antibody
Ig G	$\gamma_2\lambda_2$ $\gamma_2\kappa_2$	80% of all antibodies 8 - 16	Protect against bacteria and viruses. Crosses placenta to provide immune protection in new born
Ig M	$\mu_2\lambda_2$ $\mu_2\kappa_2$	5-10% of all antibodies 0.5 - 2	Serves as antigen receptors. Antibodies of ABO blood groups
Ig A	$\alpha_2\lambda_2$ $\alpha_2\kappa_2$	10-15% of all antibodies 1.4 - 4.2	Localized protection on mucous membrane
Ig D	$\delta_2\lambda_2$ $\delta_2\kappa_2$	0.2% of all antibodies <0.04	Involves in activation of B cells
Ig E	$\varepsilon_2\lambda_2$ $\varepsilon_2\kappa_2$	0.1% of all antibodies < 0.007	In allergic reaction, provides protection against parasite and worms

DIVERSITY OF ANTIBODY

How the diversity of antibody is genetically determined ?

- The genes for the κ and λ light chains are located on chromosome 2 and 22 respectively. However, the gene for heavy chain is located on chromosome 14.
- The amino acid sequence of variable region is about 115 amino acid long at the amino terminal end. These sequences of both heavy and light chains in the variable region are different in each type of antibody. The carboxyl terminal end consists of a constant C region of approximately 110 amino acids in the light chains (κ and λ). However, the constant region of heavy chain is three to four times longer than light chain.
- The restriction map study of the DNA segments (which are responsible for coding of C and V regions of λ or κ light chains) has shown that DNA segment coding for V region is separate from that of C region. The intermediate portion of DNA segment between V and C coding regions codes for a joining (J) region which joins the variable (V) and constant (C) portions of polypeptide chain.
- It was revealed from similar studies that the heavy chain has a fourth region i.e. diversity or D region, which is placed between V and J regions (Fig. 10.4). Each coding region of DNA segments (V, D, J and C) are separated by noncoding DNA sequences.

- A large number of DNA segments codes for variable region of the chain. The number of DNA segments coding for D, J and C regions of the chain are relatively few (Fig. 10.4).
- These coding DNA segments for V, D, J and C regions of the antibody molecule can be called as genes.
- In a single antibody molecule a single type of DNA segment (gene) is expressed for each region (V, D, J and C). For example for the formation of heavy chain only one DNA segment (gene) out of 86 is expressed from variable region (V); 1 out of 30 from D region; 1 out of 9 from J region and 1 out of 11 from C region. Thus a single heavy chain is coded by 4 different genes. And the recombination of various DNA coding segments of each region gives diversity to immunoglobulin chains.
- For the formation of heavy chain any one of the variable (V) region can be **spliced** on to any one of (D) regions which inturn spliced on to any J region. This splicing process is called V-D-J joining (Fig. 10.4). This is followed by joining of constant portion of heavy chains (any one type of gene out of Cμ, Cδ, and Cγ and so on).

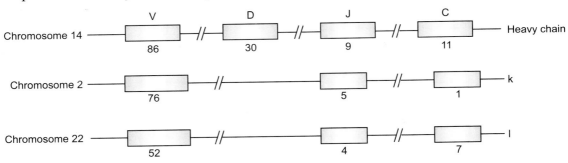

Fig. 10.4: *Diagram showing various DNA segments coding for light and heavy chains. (V=Variable region; D=Diversity region; J=Junctional region and C=Constant region.)*

- The splicing of V, D, J and C genes is then followed by transcription which itself is followed by RNA processing. In the RNA processing all the intervening sequences are removed.

The processed mRNA represents a piece meal gene containing all four adjacent coding regions (V, D, J and C). This messenger RNA in corresponding B cell will thus produce heavy chain with variable (VDJ) and constant part (C).

Thus the variability of antibody is because:
1. The large number of combinations between large number of genes of variable regions of heavy and light chains are responsible for antibody diversity.
2. Splicing of genes can also create altered codons at the splice junction which is an additional source of variation.
3. Somatic mutation of antibody genes.

IMMUNODEFICIENCY DISEASES

Immunodeficiency diseases occur due to lack of function of T cells, B cells or both. Patients who lack T cell function suffer viral infection and can accept mismatched skin transplants. Patients who lack B-cell function suffer from bacterial infection and accept mismatched blood transfusion. Some common immunodeficiency diseases are as under.

Severe combined immunodeficiency

(Swiss type autosomal recessive agammaglobulinaemia)

In this disorder both kinds of immunity (cellular and humoral) are affected. Patients are susceptible to both viral and bacterial infections (see also "The first gene therapy"-Ch. 13).

Genetics:

It is an X-linked or autosomal recessive disorder. There is deficiency of the enzyme **adenosine deaminase**. In few cases this disorder may be also due to mutation of T cell receptor and defect in other receptors. These children also may have deficiency of granulocytes. Thymus may be absent or reduced in size. Patients usually have low IgA and IgM levels.

Treatment:

- Antibiotics
- Bone marrow transplantation
- Enzyme replacement for ADA deficiency/DEG-ADA injections.
- Gene therapy

X-linked severe combined immunodeficiency

(Swiss type x-linked agammaglobulinemia)

This kind of disorder occurs commonly in males and is due to immunological stem-cell disorder. There is lack of both B-cell and T-cell functions. Abnormal cellular immunity is associated with increased susceptibility to virus infections. There is also reduced resistance to bacterial infections due to deficient Ig synthesis.

Genetics:

It is an x-linked disorder which is due to mutation in the g chain of interlukin (IL)-2 receptor.

Treatment:

Due to reduced resistance to infections death used to occur in infancy. However, now with modern antibiotics patients may survive for prolonged periods. Bone marrow transplantation is helpful.

Burton agammaglobulinemia

This disease is associated with dimnished lymphoid tissues. Tonsils and adenoids may remain absent. The B lymphocytes are very few or absent. Due to absence of B lymphocytes there is deficiency of immunoglobulins. Infants suffer from multiple recurrent bacterial infections of the respiratory tract and skin.

Genetics:

It is an x-linked disorder hence, male children are affected. The disease is due to mutation in a tyrosine kinase specific B cells.

Treatment:

- Antibiotics
- Use of intravenous immunoglobulins

Thymic agenesis

(Di George Syndrome)

The disease is due to absence of thymus gland. The absence of thymus is associated with non development of parathyroids which is due to abnormalities of III and IV pharyngeal pouches. The disease is characterised by severely reduced or absent T lymphocytes. Because of reduced cellular immunity children get recurrent viral infections. The patient may also have congenital heart disease and suffer from tetany.

Genetics:

There is deletion of a particular region of the long arm of chromosome 22.

Treatment:

Transplantation of fetal thymus.

TRANSPLANTATION OF TISSUES

The immune system does not responds to the self antigens but responds to nonself antigens. When any tissue or organ is transplanted from a donor to an unrelated recipient, the lymphocytes of recipient will recognize the nonself antigens and tissue will be rejected. The transplants between identical twins and tissues from one part of an individual's body to another part can be done without the fear of rejection as cells and tissues have identical antigens. However, besides identical twins, in all other instances the similarity of antigens of donor and recipient has to be assessed before tissue transplantation. The antigen similarity is called **histocompatibility**. In **tissue typing** the major and minor histocompatibility antigens (vide infra) of donor and recipient tissues are tested for their similarity (histocompatibility). If a donor has antigens which are not present on the cells of recipient then the recipient will reject the graft.

Genetics:

The antigenic determinants of a cell are present on its surface. These antigens are genetically determined by alleles which are located at different loci (more than a dozen). These loci are known as **histocompatibility loci**. A locus produces a specific antigen. Each histocompatibility loci has many alleles in the human population, therefore each individual has a unique combination of alleles. Thus combination of epitopes (antigenic determinants) on the cells of individual is also unique. However, some histocompatibility loci elicit stronger immune response as compared to others. In human one locus is more important than others and is called as **major histocompatibility complex (MHC)**. There are many other minor loci. The MHC locus plays important role in histocompatibility as compared to minor loci. The incompatibility at minor histocompatibility loci can be treated with **immunosuppressive drugs**. The human MHC locus is called as **HLA** (human leucocyte antigen as it was first observed on white blood cells) which is situated on chromosome 6 while minor loci are scattered throughout the genome.

The HLA locus is very complex and is divided in four regions HLA-A, HLA-B, HLA-C and HLA-D. Each region has its own series of alternative "alleles" (Table 10.2).

Each chromosome 6 has one allele for each ABCD region. The particular HLA alleles which an individual carries on each of his two chromosomes 6 is termed **haplotype**. The different combination of

Table 10.2 *Number of alleles for various types of HLA locus.*

HLA Locus	No. of Alleles
A	57
B	111
C	34
D	228

these various alleles on both chromosomes 6 give rise to a large number of HLA phenotypes. Two unrelated individuals are therefore much different in their HLA phenotypes. On other hand members of a sib (brothers and sisters) and close relatives are more likely to have antigenic similarity.

HLA typing of donor and recipient is carried out before tissue transplantation by using PCR (see chapter 15).

HLA and disease association

It is observed that various diseases are associated with a particular type of HLA. This might be due to the fact that genes for these diseases are closely linked to HLA complex. Some example of these diseases are listed in Table 10.3.

It is not necessary that an individual with particular type of HLA will always suffer from the associated disease. However, the individual has a greater relative risk of being affected as compared to general population. For example an individual who has haplotype carrying B27 allele have an 88 fold increased risk of developing the ankylosing spondylitis as compared with non-B27 individual (Table 10.3).

| Table 10.3 | Association of some diseases with particular HLA haplotypes. |

Disease	HLA	Relative risk
Ankylosing spondylitis	B27	88
Rheumatoid Arthritis	DR4	16
Ulcerative Colitis	B5	9
Juvenile diabetes	DR3/DR4	4
Hodgkin disease	A1, B5, B8, BW18	1-2

SUMMARY

- The human body has an unique ability to resist the infection of micro-organism. This ability is called immunity.
- There are two different kinds of immunity i.e. T-cell immunity and B-cell immunity.
- T-cell immunity is achieved through various kinds of T-cell (killer, suppressor and helper) which are capable to destroy the foreign invaders.
- B-cell immunity is achieved with the help of B lymphocytes. B-lymphocytes are transformed to plasma cells which produce antibodies.
- **Antibody** or **immunoglobulin** is a protein synthesized by plasma cells in response to foreign substance.
- An **antigen** is a foreign macromolecule which is capable of eliciting antibody formation.
- An **antigenic determinant (epitope)** is an identifiable feature on the surface of antigen which can be recognized by B or T cell.
- The antibody is made up of four polypeptide chains. Two of these chains are called **heavy (H)** chains and remaining two are called **light (L)** chains. These chains are interconnected with each other with the help of disulfide bonds.
- The tips of H and L chains consist of **variable (V) region** which is antigen binding site. This region is different for each kind of antibody and is capable to recognise and to provide attachment to a particular antigen.
- There are five different classes of antibodies (immunoglobulins) i.e. Ig G, Ig A, Ig M, Ig D and Ig E.
- The aminoacid sequences of both heavy and light chains in the variable region are different in every type of antibody. This is due to the fact that a large number of DNA segments codes for variable region of heavy and light chains.
- The antigenic determinants (epitopes) of a cell are present on its surface. Before tissue transplantation, the similarity of antigenes of donor and recipient has to be assessed. The antigen similarity is called **histocompatibility**.
- The antigens are genetically determined by alleles which are located at different loci. These are called **histocompatibility loci**.
- Each individual has a unique combination of alleles and thus epitopes on the cells of an individual are also unique.
- In human one locus is more important than others and is called **Major Histocompatibility Complex (MHC)**. This locus is also called as **HLA** (human leucocyte antigen). This locus is situated on chromosome number 6.

11 Genetics of Cancer

- What is Cancer?
- Growth Factors and Growth Factor Receptors in Cancer
- Cell Division Cycle Control and Cancer
- Viruses and Cancer Genes
- Apoptosis

Cancer is a dreaded disease and its incidence is on the rise. It has been estimated that about 10 million new cases of cancer and 6.4 million deaths due to cancer occur every year globally. It is suspected that the incidence and death rate from cancer in India will rise by a factor of 3 between the years 1991 and 2025 simply as a function of ageing.

WHAT IS CANCER?

Cancer is a disorder involving dynamic changes in the genome which leads to the following:

1. *Uncontrolled cellular proliferation* - Cancer cells are those cells which have lost the usual control over their growth and division. This unrestrained growth and division of the cancer cells interferes with the normal functioning of the body.
2. *Transformation* - The cancer cells are transformed cells. They are phenotypically different from normal cells. Transformed cells becomes independent of factors usually needed for cell growth.
3. *Ability to invade* - Cancer cells have ability to invade the surrounding healthy tissue.
4. *Metastasis* - Cancer cells have characteristic to disperse from the site of origin and travel to a distant parts of the body.

5. *Suppression of apoptosis* - The programmed cell death **(apoptosis)** is highly suppressed in cancer cells.
6. *Angiogenesis* - Cancer cells have ability to induce vascularization of the tumour in order to receive oxygen and nutrients.

Aetiological factors of cancer may be classified as environmental and genetical. Almost 80% of all human cancers have a large environmental component, and are therefore preventable.

Environmental factors of cancer

*   Chemicals
*   Radiations
*   Viruses
*   Bacteria, fungi and parasites
*   Hormones

Many chemicals like polycyclic aromatic hydrocarbons (3, 4 benzpyrene), aromatic amines (B-napthylamine), vinyl chloride and arsenical compounds are known carcinogens and may cause the cancers of lung, skin, bladder and liver.

Similarly, ultraviolet light (exposure to sunlight) is a common carcinogen for skin cancer (malignant melanoma and basal cell carcinoma) in fair skin people. High dose of ionizing radiation is well known carcinogen especially in people working with radioactive materials. Ionizing radiation is responsible for leukemia and cancers of skin, thyroid, bone and breast.

Many viruses are considered as strong carcinogenic agents. About 15% of all human cancers are due to viruses. Following human tumours have the known viral etiology i.e., infection of Human papilloma virus causes carcinoma of cervix; Epstein-Barr viruses are responsible for the Burkitt's lymphoma and nasopharyngeal carcinoma; Hepatitis C and B virus produces liver cancer and RNA retrovirus leads to T-cell leukemia and lymphoma. (*Association of virus and cancer is described in detail later in this chapter*).

Cancer may also result from infection with bacteria (H. pylori can produce lymphoma), toxins of fungi (aflatoxins can cause cancer of liver) and parasite like schistosoma can cause bladder cancer.

Various hormones like estrogens, androgens and steroids are now suspected as carcinogenic and may be responsible for the cancer of liver, mammary gland and endometrium.

Why and how an environmental carcinogen produces cancer?

The production of cancer by a carcinogen is a multi step process.

*   In the first step, due to presence of carcinogen, there occurs the lesion in cell's genome (in the DNA of the target cell), which leads to the transformation of the cell.
*   In the second step this transformed cell divides repeatedly (clonal proliferation). The uncontrolled cellular proliferation is the main event in the production of carcinoma.

- In the third step the clonal proliferation of tumour cells acquire autonomous growth i.e., they no longer require the stimulation by carcinogen and rapidly proliferate themselves.
- In later stages tumour cells acquire the ability to invade the surrounding tissue, metastasize at distance places in the body and induce the vascularization of the tumour.

What is cell proliferation and how is it controlled?

The main feature of cancer is the unrestricted cell proliferation. Thus cancer is due to loss of the normal mechanism which control cellular proliferation and differentiation. And so to understand cancer we need to understand what is cell proliferation and how is it controlled? The cell proliferation and differentiation is controlled by the following steps:

- Growth factor binds to a specific receptor on cell membrane.
- Growth factor receptor becomes active and in turn activates signal transducing proteins on the inner surface of plasma membrane.
- Signal is then transmitted to nucleus through cytoplasm.
- In nucleus the DNA transcription is initiated by activation of transcription factors.
- Cell enters into mitosis which ultimately results in cell division.

All the above steps of cells proliferation are controlled by genes. Any mutation in these genes may lead to unrestricted proliferation of cells. Thus, to understand the mechanism of uncontrolled cellular proliferation it is necessary to understand about the normal mechanism of cell proliferation.

THE ROLE OF GROWTH FACTORS, GROWTH FACTOR RECEPTORS AND SIGNAL TRANSDUCING PROTEINS IN CELL PROLIFERATION

The growth factors (GF) and growth factor receptors (GFR) play an important role in the normal process of growth and differentiation. Growth factors are different for different cells e.g. the epidermal growth factor (EGF) stimulates epidermal cells; fibroblast growth factor (FGF) stimulates fibroblasts; platelet derived growth factor (PDGF) stimulates proliferation of connective tissue etc. On the cell surface there are specific growth factor receptors. The binding of rowth factor to its growth receptor stimulates cell to grow in a process known as **signal transduction**. Signal transduction is a process whereby extracellular growth factors regulate cell growth and differentiation by a complex pathway. This pathway consists of many steps and each step is genetically determined.

- When a growth factor binds to its specific receptor it leads to activation of the receptor.
- The activated receptor in turn activates a series of cytoplasmic proteins. These proteins are called as **signal transducing proteins**. Many of such proteins are present on inner surface of plasma membrane.

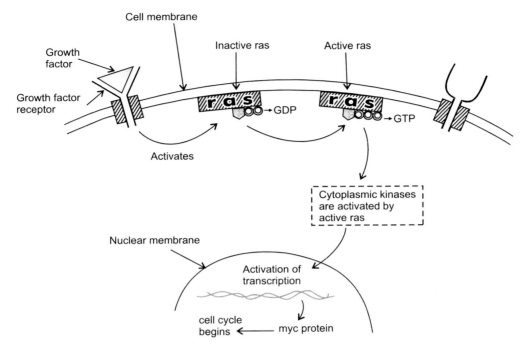

Fig. 11.1: *When in a normal cell a growth factor binds to a growth factor receptor, it gets simulated. The inactive (GDP-bound) ras is activated (GTP-bound) and sends growth signals to nucleus by activating the cytoplasmic kinases. Expression of myc proteins begins cell cycle.*

- Two important proteins of this category are produced by **ras** and **abl** genes.
- The **ras** family of proteins binds GDP (guanosine diphosphate) when cells remain in resting state.
- When cells are stimulated by growth factor then inactive **ras** becomes active by releasing GDP and binding to GTP (guanosine triphosphate) (Fig. 11.1).
- The active **ras** in turn activates cytoplasmic kinases which pass signals to nucleus for cell proliferation.
  [However, the activated stage of **ras** protein remains for a very short duration as enzyme guanosine triphosphatase (GTPase) hydrolyzes GTP to GDP. Thus the **ras** proteins becomes inactive which in turn fails to activate cytoplasmic kinases. Now no more signals for cell proliferation pass to the nucleus. The **abl** gene, similar to **ras** gene, also encodes signal transducer protein. This gene is located on chromosome 9.]
- When activated cytoplasmic kinases enter the nucleus they activate a large number of genes that regulate transcription of DNA (**myc, myb, jun, fos** and **rel gene**).
- The **myc** protein is most commonly involved and after receiving the signal to divide it binds to DNA (Fig. 11.1).

- This leads to transcriptional activation of several growth related genes including **cyclin D** (see later in cell cycle). The level of **myc** protein decline to basal level once the cell cycle begins.

How the genes coding for growth factors, growth factor receptors, signal transducing proteins and nuclear transcription factors cause cancer?

Abnormalities in growth factor signalling pathways can lead to abnormal growth. The overexpression of growth factors can lead to non-neoplastic disorders like **psoriasis**. Mutation in growth factor receptors can lead to **insulin-resistant diabetes** (insulin receptor) and **dwarfism** (fibroblast growth factor receptor). However, the carcinogenesis is a multistep process. Among the events that can lead to cancer formation is unregulated expression of growth factors or components of other signalling pathways. This is due to mutation in genes that regulate these events. These mutant genes are called as **oncogenes**. Oncogenes are genes that when activated or "turned on" may lead the malignant phenotype.

ONCOGENES

Oncogenes are genes that when "activated" are responsible for production of cancer. Non-activated oncogenes are normal genes that are involved in coding for proteins, which act as growth factors, growth factor receptors, signal transducing proteins or transcription factors. These genes are called "**proto-oncogenes**". Following are the well known proto-oncogenes: *Cyclin D, Cdk4, EFGR (epidermal growth factor receptor), FGFR (fibroblast growth factor receptor), Ras, Bcl2 and Mdm2.*

A non-activated proto-oncogene is transformed to activated oncogene by *point mutation, chromosomal translocation* or *viral infection*. The activated oncogenes induce cellular proliferation and therefore tumour development. Based on the function of proteins produced by oncogenes these can be divided into five groups:

- **Growth factor oncogenes** e.g., *sis* gene which codes for platelet derived growth factor.
- **Growth factor receptor oncogenes** e.g., *erb B* gene which codes for epidermal growth factor receptor.
- **Cyclic nucleotide binding oncogenes** e.g., *ras* and *GTP*.
- **Tyrosine kinase activity oncogenes** e.g., *src*.
- **Transcription factor oncogenes** e.g., *myc*.

TUMOUR SUPPRESSOR GENES (TSG)

It has been stated earlier that a normal cell contains proto-oncogenes that promote cell growth. Similarly, a normal cell also contains genes which are called tumour suppressor genes. The function of these genes is to apply breaks to cell growth thus they possess tumour suppressor activity. These genes check undue cell proliferation and if DNA is damaged they induce the repair of damaged DNA. These kind of TSG are thus called *"caretaker genes"* (BRCA 1, BRCA 2, MLH 1). If damaged DNA can not be repaired then they induce the cell death (apoptosis). These kind of TSG are called *"gatekeeper genes"* (p53, p21, Rb 1, Bax, APC). If these genes are lost or become inactive then cells are liberated from the constraints imposed by these genes, yielding the unconstrained growth and division. The activation of proto-oncogenes or inactivation of tumour suppressor genes both are responsible for the progression of many tumour to full malignancy. The tumour suppressor genes are a class of cellular genes whose normal function is to suppress inappropriate cell proliferation. These genes are intimately involved in the control of cell cycle. Therefore development of cancer is due to loss of function or mutation in both the copies of TSG genes. Thus tumour suppressor genes are recessive in nature.

Over 100 oncogenes and about 30 TSG are now known. Some of these genes are listed in Table 11.1 and 11.2. Some of well-known tumour suppressor genes are **BRCA-1**, **WT-1**, **Rb** and **p53**. The description of few TSGs and mechanism by which loss of their function leads to cancer transformation is described in next section (cell cycle and cancer) of this chapter.

*The analysis of functions of various known oncogenes and TSG has shown that they code for growth factor, growth factor receptors, adapter molecules, protein kinase, nuclear transcription factors, cell cycle genes, various checkpoints of cell cycle and apoptosis. Any impairment in the functioning of the above components of **signal transduction cascade** will lead to the over proliferation of cells which ultimately will result in tumour formation.*

1. *Growth factors and cancer:*
   Genes that code for growth factors, after mutation may acquire oncogenic properties. For example gene for PDGF after mutation over expresses the growth factor which give rise to cancers like **osteosarcoma** and **astrocytoma** (Table 11.1).
2. *Growth factor receptors and cancer:*
   Mutation and pathological overexpansion of growth factor receptor genes have been detected in several tumours. Due to this mutant receptor provides continuous signals for cell growth and proliferation, even in the absence of growth factor.
3. *Signal-transducing proteins and cancer:*
   Mutation of the **ras** gene (which produce signal transducing protein that attaches to inner surface of plasma membrane) is responsible for almost 30% of human tumors. Due to mutation of ras gene the GTPase is unable to hydrolyse the GTP to GDP. Thus

active ras protein remains active and cell continue to proliferate. Similarly, the mutation of GTPase protein fails to restrain the normal ras protein and result in cancer.

4. *Transcription factor and cancer:*

The mutation of genes that regulate the transcription of DNA are associated with cancer. The **myc** gene binds to DNA and activates many genes involved in growth. When this gene is mutated its overexpansion contribute to sustained proliferation. The Table 11.1 briefly mention the association of various cancers in relation to signal transduction cascades.

CELL DIVISION CYCLE CONTROL AND CANCER

The cell cycle

The cell division cycle is the process by which a cell grows, replicates its DNA and then divides to give two daughter cells. This process is divided into four sequential phases (Fig. 11.2).

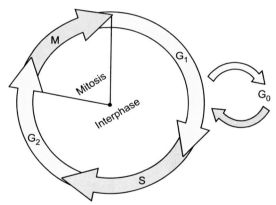

Fig. 11.2: *The cell cycle consistd of four phases i.e. G_1 (Gap phase), S (Synthesis phase), G_2 (Gap phase), M (Mitosis phase) and G_0 (when cell ceases division). Interphase of a cell consists of G_1, S, G_2 phases. Mitosis phase gives rise to two daughter cells.*

- *G1 phase* (Gap phase or pre-synthetic phase) - During this phase chromosomes become thin and extended. In this phase cell is responsive to both positive and negative growth signals. When cell is resting or has lost capability to divide (as in case of neurons) they remain in **GO** phase.
- *S phase* (Synthetic phase) - In this phase DNA replication occurs.
- *G2 phase* (pre-mitotic phase) - It is of short duration where chromosome begins to condensed in the preparation of next cell division.
- *M phase* (mitosis phase) - Here cell divides into two daughter cells.

Table 11.1 *Association of growth factors, growth factor receptors, signal transducers and transcription factors genes and human cancers.*

S.No.	Category	Gene	TS/ONC	Mechanism of activation	Associated human cancer
1.	**Growth factors** PDGF	Sis	ONC	Over expression	Osteosarcoma, astrocytoma
	FGF	hst-1, int-2	ONC	Over expression	Metanoma, breast, urinary bladder, stomach
2.	**Growth factor receptors** EGFR family	erb-B-1	ONC	Over expression	Squamous cell carcinoma of oesophagus
		erb-B-2	ONC	Over expression or amplification	Breast, ovary, stomach, lung
		egf-R	ONC	Amplification	Glioma, breast, Head and Neck
	PDGFR	pdgf-RB	ONC	Chimeric genes bacause of chromosomal translocation permanently activated receptors	Chronic myeloid leukemia Acute myeloblastic leukemia
3.	**G.T.P. binding protein**	ras	ONC	Mutation	Pancrease, lung, colon
4.	**Non-receptor tryosine kinases**	c-abl	ONC	Translocation	Chronic myelocytic leukemia
		src	ONC	Mutation	Tumours of large intestine
5.	**Transcription factors**	dpc 4	TS	Mutation or deletion	Colon, Neuroblastoma
		ctnn B1	ONC	Mutation	Colon
		myc	ONC	Gene amplification chromosomal translocation	Burkitts lymphomas, lung, neuroblastoma

Cell cycle checkpoints

The transition from one phase to the next is regulated at number of positions within the cell cycle. These positions are known as checkpoints (Fig. 11.3). The functions of checkpoints is to see that the integrity of the genome remains intact and to monitor the cellular environment. Following are the cheek points of the cell cycle.

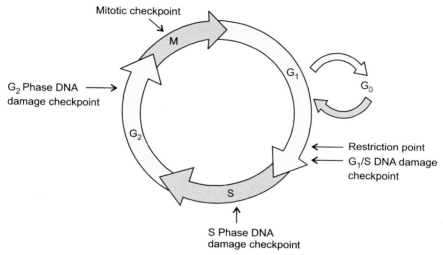

Fig. 11.3: *Various checkpoints of the cell cycle.*

- *Restriction point* - This restriction point (R) occurs between mid and late G1. At this point cell ascertains whether it has received the necessary growth signals so that it can go to S phase and replicate its DNA to complete cell division. If growth signals are sufficient then the cell will go into S phase otherwise it will enter GO phase. It is an essential control point which restrains cell proliferation.
- *G1/S DNA damage checkpoint* - This occurs at the G1/S phase transition and is a major sensor of DNA damage.
- *S phase DNA damage check point* - This check point may arrest the cell cycle in later part of S phase if there is DNA damage or incomplete DNA replication.
- *G2/M check point* - This is again a DNA damage check point.
- *Centrosome duplication check point* - A defect in the centrosome duplication or segregation arrest cells at G2/M transition.
- *Mitotic check point* - This occurs in M phase and checks the formation of mitotic spindles. A chromosome that is not attached at spindle blocks the onset of anaphase.

How cell division cycle is controlled ?

The animal cell cycle is controlled by many **cdk-cyclin complexes**. Cdk (cyclin dependent kinase) are catalytic subunits and belongs to a family of **kinases**. These kinases are known as *cyclin dependent kinases* (cdks) because their activity is dependent on **cyclins**.

Cyclins are regulatory subunits. There is always pairwise association between catalytic and regulatory subunits. Thus a specific cdk will have full activity when its cyclin partner is expressed. For example, in G1 phase cdk4 and cdk6 are acting in association with cyclin subunits D1, D2 and D3, while cdc2/cyclin B complex (cdc = cell division cycle) is expressed in G2/M phase of cell cycle (Fig. 11.4).

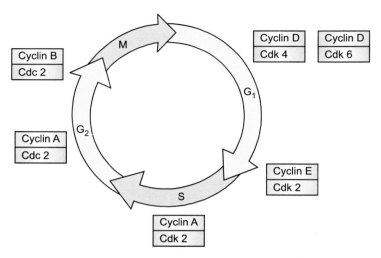

Fig. 11.4: *Control of cell division cycle. Various cyclin dependent kinase (Cdk) and cyclin are active and required at different phases of the cell cycle.*

Various proteins act as key regulator protein during cell cycle. The role of cdks is to control the cell cycle progression through phosphorylation of these regulator proteins. For example the product of retinoblastoma (RB) tumour suppressor gene (pRb) is a key regulator protein of G1 phase that is phosphorylated by cdk/cyclin complex.

* During resting phase (or during first part of G1 phase) pRb is bound to E2F. E2F is a transcription factor which is needed for cell cycle to pass from G1 to S phase (Fig. 11.5).
* Because of the fusion of pRb with E2F, S phase can not be initiated. This is due to the fact that pRb-E2F complex represses the transcription of other genes.
* Thus the cell remains in G1 phase or G0 phase.
* When growth factors stimulate cells to re-enter the cycle from G0 or G1 phase then synthesis of D cyclin is activated.
* The cdk-cyclin complexes now becomes active. The cdk 4/cyclin D and cdk6/cyclin D become active in early phase of G1 and cdk2/cyclin E complex acts in late phase of G1.
* These cdk/cyclin complex phosphorylate protein pRb.
* Because of phosphorylation of pRb, E2F is released (Fig. 11.5).
* E2F then activates transcription of genes whose functions are required for S phase.
* Repression of genes by pRb-E2F complex is also released.
* Because of inactivation of pRb cell now enters in S phase.

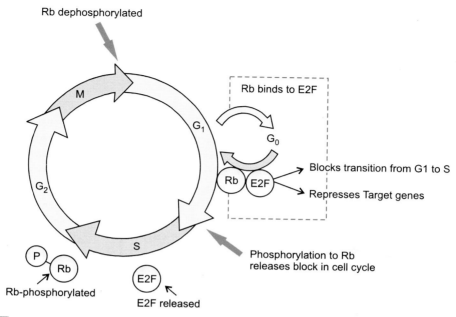

Fig. 11.5: *In a normal resting cell Rb binds to E2F which blocks its transmission from G1 to S phase and cell remains in G0. Cdk/Cyclin combination phosphorylate the Rb and E2F is released, thus cell cycle enters in S phase.*

The other mechanism by which cells can be maintained in G1 or G0 phase is by inhibition of cdk-cyclin kinases. When these inhibitor proteins binds to cdk/cyclin complex they make these complexes inactive. Thus cdk/cyclin complex is now not available to phosphorylate pRb. Because of this cells fails to enter S phase. These cdk/cyclin inhibitor proteins fall into two classes.

- *INK4 family* (Inhibitors of cdk4 family) - These proteins binds specifically to cdk4 and cdk6. It has four members; p16, p15, p18 and p19.
- *Cip or Kip family* (cdk interacting protein or kinase inhibitory protein) - This family has three members: p21, p27 and p57. p21 is a universal cdk inhibitor as it binds to all complexes of cdk2, cdk4 and cdk6. Thus it can block cell cycle at all stages of G1 and S.

Cell cycle checkpoints and cancer

Cell cycle checkpoints are under genetic control. There are number of key genes that participate in multiple cell cycle check points. These genes are called "**Gate keepers**" which prevent cell cycle progression until the damaged DNA is repaired. Any alteration (mutation) in these genes will lead to the formation of tumours due to unrestrained cell proliferation (Table 11.2).

Table 11.2   *Association of cell cycle genes and cancers.*

S.No.	Category	Gene	TS/ONC	Mechanism of activation	Associated human cancer
1.	Cdk inhibitor	p16/p15	T.S.	Mutation or deletion	Melanomas, lung
		Rb	T.S.	Mutation or deletion	Retinoblastoma, lung
		Cyclin D1	ONC	Over expression	Oesophagus, breast
2.	Transcription factor	p53	T.S.	Mutation or deletion	More than 50% of all human cancers
3.	Transcription regulator	br ca1/ br ca2	T.S.	Mutation or deletion	Breast, ovary
		VHL	T.S.	Mutation or deletion	Renal cell, pancreas

1. G1 phase

In this phase of cell cycle the cyclin D-dependent kinases act as integrators of extracellular signals for progression of cell cycle. Thus any alteration in singling pathways may lead to unrestrained cell proliferation. pRb and cyclin D-dependent kinases itself may lead to inappropriate phosphorylation and inactivation of pRb which inturn leads to misregulation of restriction point. This may leads to tumour progression.

In **mantle cell lymphoma** cyclin D1 was identified as **BCL1** gene which was found at t (11: 14) translocation. In breast, lung and glioma cancers amplification of the cyclin D1 locus at 11q13 has been identified. The tumour suppressor gene CDKN2 is either deleted or mutated in multiple cancers.

Cancer occurs also due to the mutation or deletion of RB (retinoblastoma) gene.

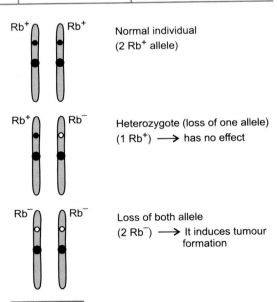

Fig. 11.6: *Retinoblastoma arises when both copies of Rb genes are inactive. Heterozygote condition is usually due to inheritance and when second copy is lost by somatic mutation it leads to tumour formation.*

Retinoblastoma is a tumour of retina which occurs in childhood. This disease may occur sporadically as a result of fresh mutation or may also be inherited. The retinoblastoma (RB) gene is located on q arm of chromosome 13. Retinoblastoma arises when both the copies of the RB genes are deleted or inactivated (Fig. 11.6). The retinoblastoma is due to loss of protein (pRb) which is the product of gene (RB). The loss of pRb may also give rise to other forms of cancers like osteosarcoma and lung cancer.

The product of RB gene (pRb) is a nuclear phosphoprotein that influences the cell cycle (refer - How cell cycle is controlled ?). In resting cells pRb is not phosphorylated by cdk/cyclin complex, thus it binds to E2F group of transcription factors. This pRb/E2F complex prevents cells to enter from G1 to S phase.

The non phosphorylated form of pRb can also bind certain viral tumour antigens like SV40T and E1A. Because the pRb-tumour antigen complex does not bind E2F the E2F helps the cell to pass from G1 to S phase (Fig. 11.7).

Thus the cell proliferation can be arrested if:

- pRb is not phosphorylated.
- D-cyclin is absent.
- p16, p21 and p27 inactivates cdk-cyclin complex.

The loss of above functions may lead to unrestrained growth or tumour formation.

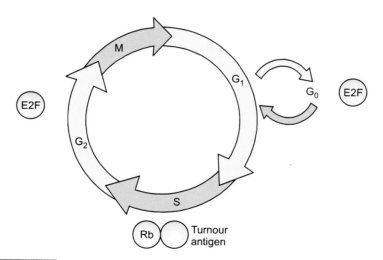

Fig. 11.7: *As tumour antigen (SV4OT, AdE1A) binds to Rb therefore E2F remains free throuout the cell cycle. This allows to cells to enter in S phase and results into unrestricted cell proliferation.*

2. *G1/S checkpoint*

This checkpoint is invoked mainly due to DNA damage caused by double strand breaks (DSBs) in the DNA. This kind of DNA damage can be brought about by ionizing radiation or genotoxic chemicals. If this DNA damage is not checked then this may lead to cancer.

The maintenance of the G1/S cell cycle checkpoint is dependent on the tumour suppressor gene (TP53). The product of this gene is p53 which acts as receiver of stress signals including DNA damage (Fig. 11.8).

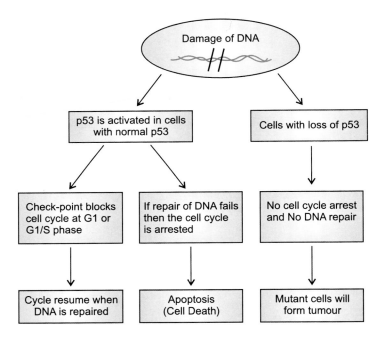

Fig. 11.8: *The gene p53 gets activated due to damage to DNA.*
p53 helps to repair DNA and if it fails the cell death (apoptosis) occurs.
In case of loss of p53 DNA damage will lead to tumour formation.

In normal cells p53 levels are low. To function as transcription factor p53 protein must be activated by phosphorylation and acetylation. Mdm2 prevents phosphorylation and acetylation of p53 and removes p53 from the nucleus. This leads to p53 degradation by the proteosome in the cytoplasm (Fig. 11.9 a and b). Thus the level of p53 remains low because Mdm2 exports p53 continuously from nucleus to cytoplasm by degradation. On the other hand if DNA damage occurs, it result in the phosphorylation and acetylation of p53. Now the Mdm2 can not bind to modified (activated) p53. So that activated p53 remains in the nucleus.

The activated p53 now triggers the transcription of a number of genes, which can invoke cell cycle arrest and apoptosis (Fig. 11.10). One of the gene p21C1P1 when induced by p53 binds to cdk2/cyclin E which leads to cell cycle arrest at G1/S

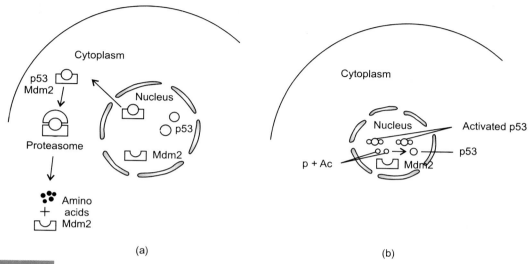

(a)   (b)

Fig. 11.9: *The p53 in a normal and DNA damaged cell. In the normal cells (a) p53 levels are low because Mdm2 removes p53 from the nucleus to cytoplasm where its degradation occurs by the proteasome. In the cells where damage to DNA has occured (b) the phosphorylation (p) and acetylation (Ac) of p53 occurs. Mdm2 can not bind to activated p53. The activated p53 now act as a transcription factor.*

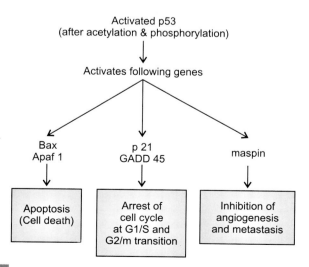

Fig. 11.10: *The activated p53 triggers the activation of many other genes.*

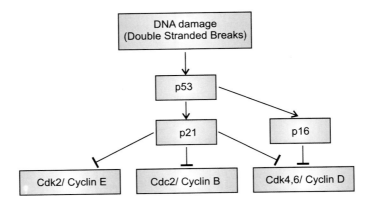

Fig. 11.11: *Several components concerned with cell cycle control are found as tumour suppressors. (→ = activation, ⊣ = inhibition).*

checkpoint (Figs. 11.11 and 11.12). Therefore p53 protein act as "**Guardian of Genome**". *The mutation in TP53 gene is responsible for about 50% cancers in human.* p53 is located on chromosome 17p13.1. Homozygous loss of the p53 gene is found in virtually every type of cancer, including carcinoma of breast, lung and colon.

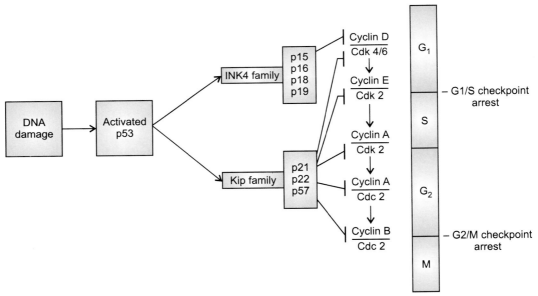

Fig. 11.12: *DNA damage results in increased level of activated p53, which in turn activates p21 protein family (Cdk/cyclin inhibitor proteins) and proteins of INK 4 family (p16 etc.). Inhibitors of INK 4 family bind specifically to Cdk 4 & Cdk 6, while p21 is a universal Cdk/cyclin inhibitor. These inhibitors block the cell cycle. (→ = activation, ⊣ = inhibition).*

Inheritance of a mutant p53 allele predisposes individuals to develop malignant tumours. These individuals are heterozygotes and said to have **Li-Fraumeni syndrome** and are at a high risk of developing a wide variety of tumours i.e. carcinomas, sarcomas, lymphomas and brain tumours.

p53 acts in the nucleus and has the ability to inhibit the cell cycle. When cell suffer from DNA damage due to exposure to chemicals or irradiation then p53 is expressed and inhibits cell cycle. The p53 protein rapidly accumulates in the nucleus and causes cells to arrest in G1 phase.

This is achieved by activation of p21 (vide supra). This arrest of cell cycle gives sufficient time for repair of DNA. At the same time p53 helps DNA repair by inducing transcription of some DNA repair enzymes. After the repair of damaged DNA the cell is allowed to complete the cell cycle. However, if repair mechanism fails then p53 stops the cell to proceed further in cell cycle. This kind of cell is then directed by p53 to undergo apoptosis.

3. *S phase*

   DNA damage during S phase invoke a cell cycle checkpoint. This checkpoint is probably dependent on dephosphorylation of pRb which blocks S phase progression. The p21 may also play role in S phase check point by inhibiting cdk activity.

4. *G2/M check point*

   This DNA damage check point function late in G2 phase by expressing Cdc2/cyclin B complex. This complex is required for progression from G2 into mitosis. The main function of the check point is to maintain Cdc2/cyclin B1 in an inactive state. Protein p53 may also play a role at this checkpoint to sustain the G2 checkpoint that leads to induction of p21 which binds and inhibits the activity of Cdc2/cyclin B in the nucleus (Figs. 11.11 and 11.12).

VIRUSES AND CANCER GENES

Our knowledge regarding genetic basis of cancer is due to viral carcinogenesis in animals. Though very few cancers in human are due to retroviruses (RNA viruses) but many type of cancers are caused by these viruses in animals. The DNA viruses also cause few types of cancer in man. The study of the genetics and replication process of retroviruses will help us to understand the process of carcinogenesis.

Retroviruses

Retroviruses carry diploid, single stranded RNA genome. They lack the autonomous replication and whenever they infect a host cell they replicate there making use of biochemical machinery of host cell (Fig 11.13). Retroviruses contain an enzyme known as **reverse transcriptase**, which makes a double stranded DNA copy of the viral RNA. This double stranded DNA copy of the viral RNA gets integrated into the chromosomal

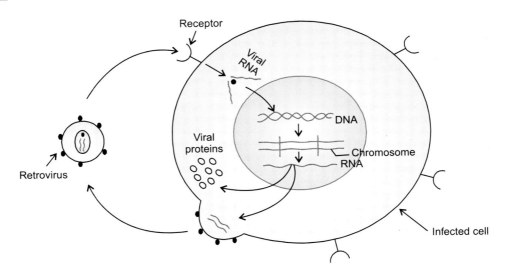

Fig. 11.13: *Replication cycle of a retrovirus.*

DNA of host cell and is called as "**provirus**". The proviral genome has only three genes necessary to ensure replication.

* **gag** - it codes for structural protein.
* **pol** - it codes for enzyme reverse transcriptase.
* **env** - it codes for protein of outer envelope.

The proviral genome carries its own promotor and enhancer elements at each end of the genome. These are known as **long terminal repeat** (LTR) (Fig. 11.14).

The replication of provirus gives RNAs that become the genome of progeny viruses. Similarly, the transcription of provirus lead to mRNA which leads to the manufacture of appropriate proteins of new progeny virons. This ultimately leads to liberation of numerous new virus particles (Fig. 11.13).

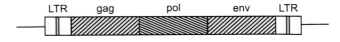

Fig. 11.14: *Genome of a retrovirus with LTR at both terminals.*

The provirus which integrates in the chromosomal DNA of a host cell remains integrated for the life time of infected cell and its progeny. On many occasions if retroviruses have infected germ line cells of host, then the DNA provirus can be passed on to the next generation through egg or sperm.

Though the genome of simple retrovirus carries the **gag, pol** and **env** genes but study of Rous sarcoma virus, identified a fourth gene which was capable of transforming a host cell to cancer cell. This gene is designated as **src** gene (Fig. 11.15). The **src** gene codes for a protein kinase and is thought to induce transformation of host cell. The viral gene which transforms the host cell is known as **oncogene**.

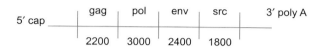

Fig. 11.15: *Genetic map of sarcoma virus.*

The oncogenes present in viruses are called viral oncogenes or **V-onc** and oncogenes present in host cells are called cellular oncogenes or **C-onc** genes.

In host cells there are DNA sequences homologous to the viral oncogenes and are called **proto-oncogens**. Proto-oncogenes are responsible for promotion of normal cell growth. Though these genes are not oncogenic in nature but have the potential to become oncogenic. The cellular proto-oncogenes can be activated to oncogenes not only by point mutation but also by amplification and chromosomal translocation.

How viral oncogenes are formed ?

It is interesting to note that retroviral oncogenes originates from cellular genes in the host. Any error in the replication of retroviral genome, after their integration in host genome, gives rise to retroviral oncogene. This viral oncogene is structurally similar to its cellular counterpart (the viral oncogene **sis** is almost similar to the gene for platelet-dependent growth factor [PDGF]) but different in its function.

How proto-oncogenes get converted to cellular oncogenes (c-onc) ?

Proto-oncogenes can be converted into cellular oncogenes in the following ways:

1. *By increase in the amount of proto-oncogene product:*

   This can be achieved in two ways.

   a. When a retrovirus integrates in the host DNA close to a proto-oncogene then its long terminal repeat (LTR) induces uncontrolled expression of proto-oncogene (Fig. 11.16). For example when Epistein - Barr viruses infect humans then over expression of **myc** gene with the LTR of virus leads to development of **Burkitt's lymphoma** in humans.

   b. Proto-oncogenes can also be activated by gene amplification i.e. by producing multiple copies of the gene. This leads to production of greater amount of oncoprotein.

In **neuroblastoma** there is amplification of **N-myc** gene. While in human lung carcinoma **c-myc**, **N-myc** and **L-myc** genes are amplified. In certain breast carcinoma there is amplification of **c-neu** or **erb**-B2 genes.

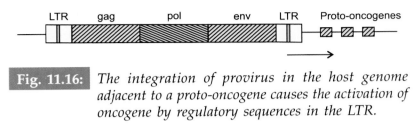

Fig. 11.16: *The integration of provirus in the host genome adjacent to a proto-oncogene causes the activation of oncogene by regulatory sequences in the LTR.*

2. *Mutation in coding sequence:*
   A proto-oncogene can be converted to oncogene by point mutation in the nucleotide sequence. About 30% of human cancers are due to mutation in **ras** gene.
3. *Chromosomal translocation:*
   Chromosomal translocation are well known to cause cancers in human. Two well known examples of these are **chronic myeloid leukaemia** and **Burkitt's lymphoma**. The white blood cells of chronic myeloid leukaemia patients contain an abnormal 22 chromosome (**Philadelphia chromosome**, ph).
   The Philadelphia chromosome results due to reciprocal translocation between long arms of 22 and 9 chromosomes. This translocation transfers cellular **abl** oncogene from chromosome 9 that fuses with **bcr** (break-point cluster region) gene of chromosome 22. This fused gene (chimaeric gene) manufactures protein that contains about 900 amino acids of **bcr** region and 1100 amino acids of **c-abl** region.
   In case of Burkitt's lymphoma there occurs the translocation of the **c-myc** gene from the long arm of chromosome 8 on to the chromosome 14. This region of chromosome 14 contains gene locus for the immunoglobulin heavy chain. Because of this translocation **c-myc** gene comes under regulatory sequences of the immunoglobulin gene which increases transcription of **c-myc** gene almost to 20 times.

THE GENETICS OF APOPTOSIS

Apoptosis or cell death is a programmed event to maintain a balance between the generation of new cells and the death of senescent or defective cells.

Cells usually die when they grow old and are unable to furnish proteins like telomerase enzyme needed to cross the check points in the cell cycle or breaks in the DNA and are directed towards self destruction. Cells also die if they are subject to sustained injuries such as heat, oxidative stress, UV, irradiation damage or get killed when infected with a virus or other intracellular pathogen that destroys the cell.

Apoptosis occurs due to several such damages that causes damage to the growth regulating genes, loss of check-point genes and also when the telomerase enzyme is unable to protect the integrity of the terminal part of the chromosomes after each cell division. (With each cell division, the tails of each chromosome gets shortened due to progressive loss of nucleotides to reach a certain limit where the cells automatically undergo self destruction. This threshold is referred as the **Hayflick's** limit. This phenomenon occurs due to gradual dwindling in the levels as well as activity of the telomerase enzyme that is needed to repair damaged ends of the chromosome.)

Thus apoptosis is a form of programmed cell death initiated by extracellular or intracellular signals in which enzymes are activated that breakdown the cytoplasmic and nuclear skeleton, degraded the chromosomes, disintegrate the DNA and shrink the cells. Apoptosis is a complex process which occurs in three steps.

- **First Step**: Initiation of the process of apoptosis due to extracellular or intracellular signals.
- **Second step**: Execution of cell death due to release of *caspases* (cysteine containing aspartase specific protease). Caspases are ultimate destroyer of cell. These are a family of pro-enzymes that are activated in a cascade. The targets of these proteases are the DNA, several cytoskeletal proteins, DNA repair enzymes etc. The caspase family includes at least 13 proteins and is divided into three groups:

   a) *nonapoptotic caspases* (1, 4, 5, 11, 12 and 13). They have no role in apoptosis.
   b) *initiator caspases* (caspases 8, 9 and 10). Once activated, the initiator caspases process and activate one or more effector caspases.
   c) *effector caspases* (caspases 2, 3, 6 and 7). These capases breaks chromosomes, cellular organelles and intracellular proteins.

- **Third step**: There occur the morphological changes in the dying cells. Surrounding cells like macrophages remove the dead cells.

Apoptosis can be initiated by extra-cellular or intracellular pathways.

Extra-cellular (extrinsic) pathways

In this pathway initiation of apoptosis is due to extracellular signals (*Ligands*) that binds cell surface receptors. This includes cytokines that activate *"death receptors"* e.g., Fas, and tumour necrosis factor (TNF). Death receptors are all members of the TNF receptor super family i.e., TRAIL (TNF related apoptosis ligand)-R1, TRAIL-R2, TNF-R1, DR3 and DR6.

The binding of Fas ligand to Fas receptor leads to clustering of Fas complexes. This activates the initiator caspase 8, which in turn initiate apoptosis by effector caspases 3, 6 and 7 (Fig. 11.17a).

Intracellular (intrinsic) pathways

The intracellular pathway encompasses response to a greater variety of inputs i.e., extracellular or intracellular factors. The mitochondria play an important intermediary in the pathway Fig. 11.17b. It acts as a storehouse of protein co-factors needed to activate

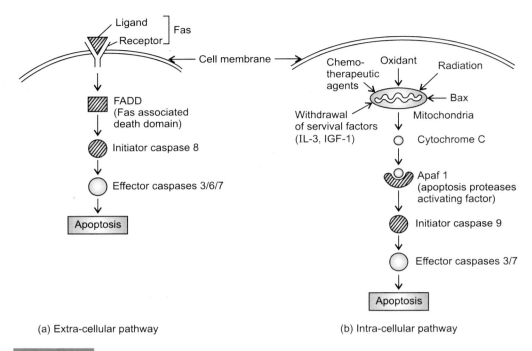

(a) Extra-cellular pathway (b) Intra-cellular pathway

Fig. 11.17: *Chain events in extra-cellular and intra-cellular pathways of apoptosis.*

the caspases. The mitochondria detect cell damage and release the pre-apoptotic enzymes and cytochrome-C. with subsequent apoptosis.

Cytotoxic drugs (anticancer drugs) and radiations (gamma and UV) damage the DNA in the nucleus. This in turn activates p53 and ultimately leads to apoptosis by the caspases. Similarly, withdrawal of survival factors like lnterlukin (IL), lnsulin like growth factor (IGF) etc. leads to activation of pro-apoptotic genes like BH3. this activates Apaf-1 and then to caspases.

The intracellular molecule like TP53 gene and its protein product (p53) acts as major initiator of apoptosis. This is achieved by the activation of effectors molecules like **Bax** and **Apaf-1** (apoptosis proteases activating factor). Bax is a pro-apoptotic molecule which normally exists in a heterodimer with an inhibitor of apoptosis called **Bcl2**.

- In normal condition, the production of Bax and Bcl2 is balanced. This balance (Bax-Bcl2 heterodimer) is a must for the existence of normal cells (Fig. 11.18).
- After the damage fo DNA p53 gets activated. This leads to increased level of Bax (Bax-Bax homodimer). This promotes apoptosis and self destruction of cells.
- On the other hand activation of oncogenes increases the level of anti-apoptotic molecule Bcl2. This prevents apoptosis. Cells in this state continue to grow and divide indefinitely. This leads to progression towards cancerous state.

As stated earlier the intracellular pathway of apoptosis is initiated by various agents (factors) like heat stress, oxidants, p53 accumulation, Bax, radiations, cytotoxic drugs etc. These agents trigger the release of cytochrome C from the mitochondria and subsequent activation of apoptotic machinery i.e., the cytochrome C combines with inactive Apaf-1 to activate it, which in turn activates initiator caspase 9. This activates the effectors caspases (3 and 7), which ultimately leads to the apoptosis (Fig. 11.17b).

The release of cytochrome is controlled by the bcl2 gene product.

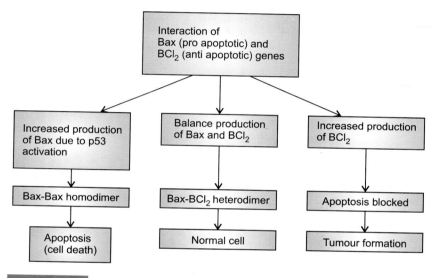

Fig. 11.18: *Flow chart showing interaction of Bax and BCl₂ genes.*

SUMMARY

- *Cancer cells have the following characteristics:*
  - Show uncontrolled proliferation.
  - Transform to abnormal cells.
  - Ability to invade surrounding tissues.
  - Metastatise to distant places.
  - Show suppression of apoptosis.
  - Induce angiogenesis.
- *Cancer is due to loss of the normal mechanism which control cellular proliferation and differentiation.*
- *Cellular proliferation is under the control of genes.*
- Genes responsible for causing cancer are know as **oncogenes**.

- Tumour suppressor genes (TSG) apply breaks to unrestrained cell growth thus they possess tumour suppressor activity. Thus cancer may develop due to loss of function (mutation) of TSG.
- About 100 oncogenes and about 30 TSGs are now known.

Growth factor and growth factor receptors in cancer.

- **Signal transduction** is a process by which extracellular growth factor regulate cell growth and differentiation by a complex of pathway. (Growth factor – activation of receptor – cytoplasmic proteins (**ras** and **abl**) are activated – ras binds to GTP – cytoplasmic kinases are activated – Kinases enter the nucleus – activate **myc** which regulate transcription of DNA – cell cycle begins)
- Genes that code for growth factors and growth factor receptors after mutation may acquire oncogenic properties.
- The mutation of ras gene (which codes for signal transducing protein) and myc gene coding for transcription factor may cause cancer.

Cell cycle control and cancer

- The cell division cycle is divided into four sequential phases i.e. G1, S, G2 and M phase.
- The transition from one phase to the next is regulated by **checkpoints**.
- Cell cycle is controlled by cdk/cyclin complexes.
- Various proteins act as key regulator protein during cell cycle. For example, the produce of **retinoblastoma (RB)** tumour suppressor gene **(pRb)** is a regulator protein of G1 phase that is phosphorylated by cdk/cyclin complex.
- Cell cycle check points are under genetic control. In case DNA (gene) is damaged, cell cycle progression is checked till the damaged DNA (gene) is repaired.
- Any alteration (mutation) in these genes will lead to the formation of tumour due to uncontrolled cell proliferation.
- The maintenance of the G1/S cell cycle checkpoint is dependent on the tumour suppressor gene (TP53). The mutation of TP53 gene is responsible for about 50% cancers in human.
- The gene p21 when induced by p53 binds to cdk2/cyclin E which leads to cell cycle arrest at G1/S check point. Thus mutation of p53 and p21 may lead to nonfunctioning of G1/S, S and G2/M check points leading to formation of tumour.

Viruses and cancer genes

- Retroviruses (RNA viruses) and DNA viruses are responsible for causing cancers in man.
- The oncogenes present in viruses are called **viral oncogenes (V-onc)** those in host cells are called **cellular oncogenes (C-onc)**. In host cells there are DNA sequences homologous to the viral oncogenes and are called **proto-oncogenes**. *Proto-oncogenes are responsible for promotion of normal cell growth.* The cellular proto-oncogenes can be activated to oncogenes by the following three methods.
    - By increasing the amount of proto-oncogene product.
    - By mutation in coding sequence.
    - By chromosomal translocation.

Genetic mechanism of neoplastic transformation

Three genetic alterations can change a normal cell to neoplastic cell:

- Telomerase expression leads to immortalization of cells (refer Chapter 3).

- Oncogene (e.g. ras) sets up autocrine growth stimulation.
- Inactivation of tumor suppressor genes (e.g., Rb, p53) removes inhibition of growth control.

Genetics of apoptosis

- DNA damage also triggers apoptosis (programmed cell death).
- Bax is a pro-apoptotic gene, while Bcl_2 is anti-apoptotic gene.
- When intracellular or extracellular apoptotic pathway is activated, a cascade of proteolysis is initiated. The proteases involved are called **caspases.**
- Action of caspases ultimately results in cell death.

12 Developmental Genetics

- Molecular Processes in Development

- Molecular Control of Early Embryonic Development

The development of a new born from a single cell (fertilized ovum) is guided by a large number of molecules (genes). These genes guide and control the various processes of embryological growth and differentiation. The development is regulated by the cascades of gene expression i.e., early acting regulatory genes initiate the developmental process- these genes then induce the expression of downstream genes until the genes that encode the actual structure of embryo are activated. Now it is also clear that the same gene may be expressed at different periods of development and in different organs. This reduces the number of genes required for the control of development.

Genes exert their influence on cellular functions by synthesis of proteins. The proteins synthesized differ from cell to cell and even within the same cell, at different time. This provides the basic mechanism for the control of the process of embryonic development.

MOLECULAR PROCESSES IN DEVELOPMENT

This chapter provides a brief introduction of the molecular basis of development. A large number of molecules are involved in the embryonic development that may be grouped into two categories i.e., some of these molecules are present out side the cell and some of these are present within the cell.

Molecules exerting influence from out side the cells act as intercellular **signaling molecules.** These molecules exert their effects on the neighboring cells or cells located at a distance. Many signaling molecules are called **growth factors.** These signaling molecules bind and act on other kind of molecules known as **receptor molecules.** Receptor molecules are usually trans-membrane protein present in the plasma membrane of the cells. The signaling molecules after combining with the receptor molecules start a series of events through which molecular signal passes from cell membrane to nucleus **(signal transduction pathway).** The molecular signal received in the nucleus through signal transduction pathway acts as a **transcription factor** which initiates the gene expression (Fig. 12.1).

The category of molecules present within the cell is known as transcription factors. These factors are gene regulatory proteins that are present in the nucleus. Transcription

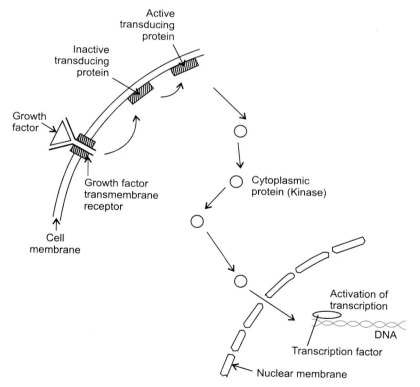

Fig. 12.1: *In the process of signal transduction a signal molecule binds to receptor on the cell membrane. Due to this an inactive transducing protein gets activated and sends a signal to the nucleus by activating a series of cytoplasmic kinases. The signal reaching the nucleus is in the form of transcription factor, that begins the transcription of the specific gene. (Courtesy of Prof. Inderbir Singh, Human Embryology, 8th edition, Macmillan.)*

factors binds to the DNA at promoter or enhancer region of the specific gene and initiate the process of transcription. The transcription factors are important molecules that guide embryological development.

(The mutation and over-expression of growth factor genes, receptor genes, signal transducing gnes and genes which codes for transcription factors are associated with various kinds of growth anomalies and cancers. For details of cancers refer Chapter 11).

1. Signaling molecules (Growth and differentiation factors)

The term *growth factor* refers to a naturally occurring protein capable of stimulating cellular proliferation and cellular differentiation. Growth factors are important for regulating a variety of cellular processes. These factors are different for different cells i.e., the epidermal growth factor (*EGF*) stimulates epidermal cells; fibroblast growth factor (*FGF*) stimulates to fibroblasts; platelets derived growth factor (*PDGF*) stimulates the proliferation of connective tissues etc.

Growth factors typically act as signaling molecules between cells in embryos. Examples are cytokines and hormones that bind to specific receptors on the surface of their target cells. As described above, the cell to cell signaling is necessary for induction of cellular differentiation. The signals by growth and differentiation factors are transmited from one cell to another by endocrine, paracrine or juxtacrine interactions.

Endocrine: These signals are called hormones, which travel through the blood to reach a distant place in the body.

Paracrine: These signals targets cells, which are present in neighborhood of emitting cell.

Juxtacrine: In this kind of signaling it is necessary that adjacent cells should be in cell to cell physical contact. The well known examples of these signaling are signals passing through "gap junction" and "notch signaling". The notch signaling is described later in this chapter.

Some common growth and differentiation factors are given in Table 12.1. A detail description of sonic hedgehog is given in box.

2. Growth factor receptors

The signaling molecules exert their effect on target cells by interacting with receptors in other cells. Most receptors are present on cell surface and are trans-membrane protein with extra-cellular, trans-membrane and cytoplasmic domain. Molecules that carry a signal to a receptor are called **ligands.** A ligand may be hormone, cytokine or growth factor. The receptor's main function is to recognize and respond to a specific ligand such as growth factors and hormones. They bind to the specific signaling molecules on the outer side of the membrane and initiate the *tyrosine kinase* activity on the inner side of the membrane. This is followed by the activation of cytoplasmic protein kinases. At present as many as 14 types of tyrosine kinase growth factor receptors are known.

Beside the transmembrane receptors, another kind of surface receptor i.e., *notch receptor* plays an important role in embryonic development. In this kind of signaling

Table 12.1   *Few common growth and differentiation factor groups and their role in development.*

Growth factors	Functions
1. **Epidermal Growth Factor (EGF)**	Growth and proliferation of cells of ectodermal and mesodermal origin.
2. **Transforming Growth Factors (TGFs)**	
TGF –B1 to TGF –B5	Forms the extra-cellular matrix, induces epithelial Branching, myoblast proliferation.
Bone Morphogenetic Factors (BMP 1 to 9)	Bone formation, cell division, cell migration and apoptosis.
Mullerian Inhibiting Factor (MIF)	Regression of paramesonephric duct
Nodal	Formation of primitive streak, right-left axial fixation, formation of mesoderm
Lefty	Determination of body asymmetry
Activin	Proliferation of granulosa cells
Inhibin	Inhibition of gonadotrophin
3. **Hedgehog proteins**	
Sonic Hedgehog, Desert, Indian,	Shh controls neural tube formation, somite differentiation, gut formation, limb development, growth of genital tubercle
4. **WNT Protein**	Mid brain development, somite and urogenital differentiation, limb patterning
5. **Fibroblast Growth Factors (FGFs)**	Mesoderm differentiation, angiogenesis, axon growth, limb development, development of various parts of brain, early liver induction, mesenchymal proliferation in jaw, induction of prostate gland, outgrowth of genital tubercle.
6. **Insulin like Growth factors (IGFs)**	IGF-1 act as factor for bone growth, IGF-2 is a fetal growth factor
7. **Nerve Growth Factor (NGFs)**	Stimulate the growth of sensory and sympathetic neurons.

(juxtacrine signaling) a protein on one cell surface interacts with a receptor on an adjacent cell surface. Notch is a cell surface receptor, which has a long extra-cellular part and a smaller intracellular part. The notch receptor becomes activated when it comes in contact with the specific protein (***delta*** or ***jagged***) present on the surface of the dominant cell.

HEDGEHOG PROTEINS

Hedgehog proteins of signaling molecules are most potent for embryological development. This family consists of molecules like Sonic hedgehog, Indian hedgehog, desert hedgehog and tiggy winkle hedgehog. The term hedgehog was derived because the mutant larvae of Drosophila contain patches of spiky outgrowths on their bellies.

Sonic hedgehog is a busy molecule in development. In a developing embryo it serve as a signaling molecule at various places i.e., notochord, neuro-ectoderm, primitive node, zone of polarizing activity in limb, genital tubercle, retina, hair buds, lung buds etc.

Sonic hedgehog-Patched – Gli pathway

Sonic hedgehog is a protein with conserved N- terminal and divergent C- terminal. All of the signaling activity of this molecule resides in its N-terminal segment. C- terminal plays no role in the signaling. Soon after the release of hedgehog protein molecule from rough endoplasmic reticulum it is auto-cleaved by the catalytic activity of its C-terminal portion. The N-terminal segment binds to cholesterol and is secreted from the cell but remains attached to cell membrane.

- On the surface of the cell, sonic hedgehog + cholesterol molecules bind to a trans-membrane receptor called as **Patched**.
- The normal action of patched is to inhibit another trans-membrane protein called **smoothened.**
- But when patched receptor binds to sonic hedgehog it inhibits the inhibitory activity of patched.
- This allows the smoothened to pass signals. Thus the signaling cascade within the cell is activated.
- This signal ultimately activates zinc finger transcription factor, **Gli.**
- Gli moves to nucleus and binds to the specific site on DNA of the target cell to express the gene (Fig 12.2).

Defect in sonic hedgehog-patched-gli pathway leads to a number of malformation syndromes.

- Mutation of sonic hedgehog gene (situated on chromosome number 7q36) causes incomplete cleavage of developing brain into right and left cerebral hemispheres and cyclopia (holoprosencephaly).
- Mutation of patched receptor (9q22) causes multiple basal cell carcinomas, bifid ribs, ovarian fibromata.
- Mutation of smoothened protein (7q31) causes basal cell carcinoma and medulloblastomas.
- Mutation of Gli (7p13) causes genital anomalies and syndactyly.

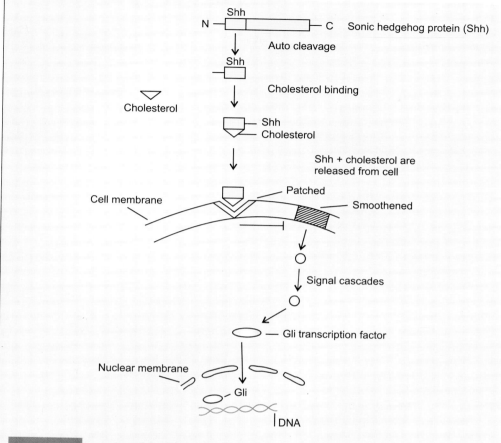

Fig. 12.2: *Schematic diagram showing Sonic hedgehog-Patched-Gli pathway. Arrows indicate activation and bar indicates inhibition. When sonic hedgehog binds to patched receptor the inhibitory effect of patched on smoothened receptor is removed. This allows smoothened to pass intracellular signals.*

This results in the activation of notch signaling pathway, which ultimately inhibits the neighboring cell from differentiating into the dominant cell (Fig. 12.3).

The notch-signaling pathway is an important mechanism of neuronal differentiation, blood vessels specification and somite segmentation. In the mechanism of neuronal differentiation, in a population of developmentally equivalent cells only few cells develop into neurons while many neighboring cell develop as glial cells. The maturing neuronal cells inhibit the maturation of neighboring cells as the dominant neuronal cells thus they develop as glial cells (Fig. 12.4) This phenomenon is known as *lateral inhibition*.

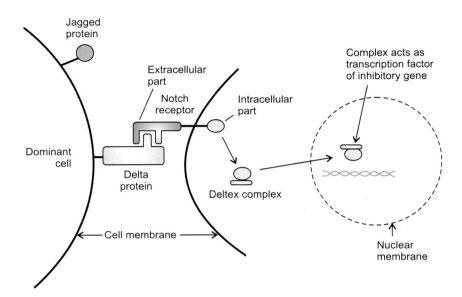

Fig. 12.3: *Diagram showing Delta-Notch pathway. In this kind of signalling the Notch receptor of a neighbouring cell binds to Delta protein present on a dominant cell. This leads to cleavage of intracellular part of the Notch receptor, which forms a Deltex complex and enters the nucleus. In the nucleus this complex acts as a transcription factor of a gene whose products repress the expression of many other genes which are required for the promotion of differentiation. This ultimately prevents the cell from differentiating into the dominant cell type. (Courtesy of Prof. Inderbir Singh, Human Embryology, 8th edition, Macmillan.)*

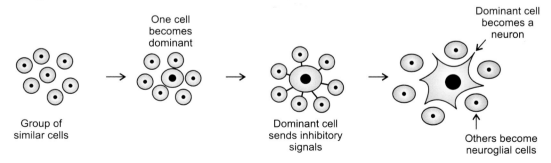

Fig. 12.4: *Diagram showing the process of lateral inhibition. Out of a group of developmentally similar cells one cell changes to a dominant type (e.g. neuron). What leads to its differentiation as a dominant cell is not known. The dominant cell gives off inhibitory signals to neighbouring cells through the notch signalling pathway. The dominant cell differentiates into a neuron while neighbouring cells develop into neuroglial cells. (Courtesy of Prof. Inderbir Singh, Human Embryology, 8th edition, Macmillan.)*

3. Signal transduction

The signal transduction is the process by which a cell converts one kind of signal into another. Signal transduction usually involves the binding of extracellular signaling molecules to receptors and triggers the sequence of biochemical reactions inside the cell. Within the cell these reactions are carried out by enzymes. Sometimes, this chain of reaction is called "**signal cascade**". The signal transduction is a process whereby extra-cellular growth factors regulate the cell growth and differentiation by a complex pathway. This pathway consists of many steps and each step is genetically determined.

- When a growth factor binds to its specific receptor it leads to the activation of receptor.
- The activated receptor in turn activates a series of cytoplasmic proteins. These proteins are called *signal transducing proteins*. Many of such proteins are present on inner surface of plasma membrane.
- The active signal trnasducing protein in turn activates cytoplasmic proteins (kinases). Thus a cascade of protein activation is established.
- This ultimately activates a transcription factor.
- The transcription factor then binds to DNA in the nucleus and activates or inhibits the expression of growth and differentiation related gene.

4. Transcription factors

The transcription factors (gene regulatory proteins) are present in nucleus. They determine the region of the DNA to be transcribed. The transcription factor along with RNA polymerase binds to the promoter region of the gene to initiate the process of transcription. These factors can switch genes on and off by activating or repressing gene expression. The transcription factor control many other genes in sequential cascades thus regulate many fundamental embryological processes like induction, segmentation, migration, differentiation and programmed cell death. A large number of transcription factors are common and found in all types of cells. However, some transcription factors are found only in certain types of cells or are active only during some stages of development.

Based on the structure of their DNA binding sites, the transcription factors are grouped together in various families. Only some of the main types are described on next page (see Table 12.2).

Basic helix-loop-helix proteins

This kind of transcription factors contain a short length of amino acids in which two alpha- helices are separated by an amino acid loop (Fig. 12.5). This kind of transcription factors are involved mainly in myogenesis (*MyoD and myogenin*).

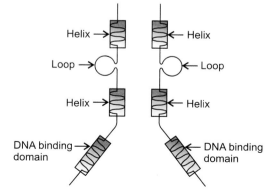

Fig. 12.5: *Domains of the basic helix-loop-helix transcription factors.*

Table. 12.2 *Transcription factor families and their function.*

	Transcription Factor Gene	Function
1.	Basic helix-loop–helix protein	Myogenesis, neurogenesis, hematogenesis, pancreas development
2.	Zinc Finger Protein	Regulates the expression of genes in kidney, gonads etc.
3.	HOX genes	Regulate segmentation, patterning of hind brain and formation of axis of the embryo.
4.	PAX Genes (paired box genes)	Sense organs (eye and ear) and nervous system development, cellular differentiation at the time of epithelial mesenchymal transition.
5.	Sox Genes (LEF-1, SRY typeHMG)	This gene is expressed in many structures during development.
6.	POU Genes (Pit-1, Oct)	Role in early cleavage.
7.	Lim proteins	Regulator of myogenic differentiation.
8.	T-BOX Genes (TBX)	Induction of mesodermal germ layer. Specification of hind v/s fore-limbs. Notochord differentiation.
9.	Dlx Genes (Dlx-1 to Dlx-7)	Involved in morphogenesis of jaw and inner ear.

Zinc finger transcription factors

This type of DNA binding domain is the zinc finger motif. In this type of proteins zinc ions binds to regularly placed cyctine and histidine unit of polypeptide chain. Because of this the polypeptide chain is puckered into fingerlike structures (Fig. 12.6). These fingers can be inserted into the specific sites of DNA helix.

These types of transcription factors are critical in the formation of kidney, gonads, hindbrain and white blood cells. The abnormalities of zinc finger genes are associated with many developmental abnormalities. Following table indicates these abnormalities.

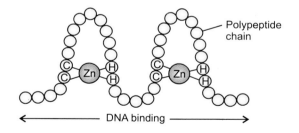

Fig. 12.6: *Structure of a zinc finger DNA-binding sequence. The binding of Zn atom to cysteine (C) and histidine (H) causes looping out of finger like structures (Zinc fingers). These fingers of transcription factor are inserted into the specific sites of DNA helix.*

Table. 12.3	Developmental abnormalities associated with the zinc finger transcription factor.	

Gene	Chromosomal location	Developmental abnormalities due to abnormal gene
GLI 3	7p13	Head, hand and foot abnormalities (polydactyly and syndactyly). Imperforated anus.
WT1	11p13	Wilms' tumor, ambiguous external genitalia
ZIC2	13q32	Holoprosencephaly
ZIC3	Xq26	Abnormal position of heart, liver and spleen.

HOX Genes

In humans, HOX genes encode a special class of transcription factors. This class of genes was originally discovered in Drosophila, in which they are called **homeotic** genes. The name homeotic was given because these genes are capable to transform one part of the body into another (i.e., mutation of one homeotic gene, the *Antennepedia* gene, leads to the growth of legs in place of antennae). This indicate that the homeotic transcription factors regulate large set of downstream genes that are responsible for the formation of body parts. The homeotic genes of Drosophila are 8 in number and are situated on chromosome number 3. These genes in Drosophila determine which embryonic segement should bear antennae, wings or legs. All 8 homeotic genes contain the same 180 base pair sequence of DNA called **homeobox**. The homeobox encodes protein **homeodomain** containing 60 amino acids. The homodomain proteins are important transcription factor that regulate the activity of many downstream genes. These homeotic genes help to establish the embryonic pattern along cephalocaudal axis, limb bud axis and genital axis.

These homeotic genes of Drosophila have been well conserved during evolution for hundreds of millions of years and are present in human and other mammals. These genes in human are called as **HOX genes**. Similar to Drosophila, HOX genes also contain homeobox. HOX genes are most closely related to the Drosophila homeotic genes in both -sequence, arrangement and functions (see later on page 170).

The homeobox has now been discovered in many other transcription factor genes (i.e., Engrailed, Paired box genes, Pou, Lim, Zinc finger and NK-2, see Fig. 12.7). These genes are situated out side the HOX gene clusters. More details about homeotic and HOX genes is described later on pages 169 to 172.

Pax Genes (Paired Box Genes)

The paired box is DNA sequence that encodes 128 amino acid DNA binding transcription regulator paired domain. The Pax gene family consists of 9 genes in humans (Pax-1 to Pax-9). Pax genes play important role in the development of eye, ear and nervous system.

The Pax gene mutations and associated developmental abnormalities are given below in Table 12.4.

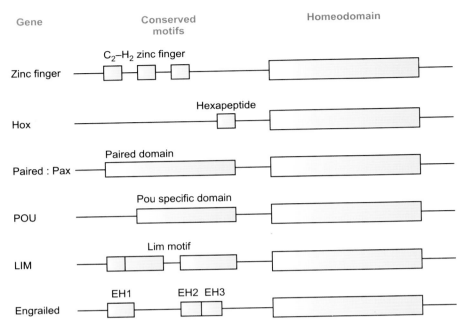

Fig. 12.7: *Diagramatic representation of homeodomain of some of homeobox containing gene classes. These gene classes also contain conserved motifs out side the homeodomain.*

Table. 12.4 *Developmental abnormalities in human due to mutation in Pax genes.*

Pex Gene	Chromosomal location	Developmental abnormalities due to mutation
Pax-2	10p25	Renal malformation and malformation of retina and optic nerve (*renal-coloboma syndrome*).
Pax-3	2q35	Loss of hearing, areas of depigmentation in hair and skin and abnormal pigmentation of iris (warrdenburg syndrome).
Pax- 6	11p13	Absence of iris (aniridia)
Pax-7	1p36	Sarcoma

SOX Genes

Sox genes contain a 79 amino acid domain that is known as HMG (high mobility group) box. Sox genes consist of over 20 members. These genes show homology with Y-linked SRY gene. SRY gene plays a major role in male sex determination. The name of this group (SOX) was derived from SRY HMG box.

The HMG domain activates transcription by bending DNA (hence, also called DNA bending protein) in such a way that other regulatory factors can also bind with promoter region of genes. Sox genes are expressed in many structures during embryogenesis. In human Sox-9 is expressed in development of skeletal tissue and regulates type II collagen. The mutation of sox-9 (situated on chromosome 17) causes bowing of long bones. The mutation of Sox-10 (on chromosome 22) causes Hirschsprung disease.

POU Genes

Pou transcription factor have both a homeodomain and a second DNA binding site (a region encoding 75 amino acids). The Pou gene family is named for the acronym of the first genes identified, i.e., Pit-1, Oct-1 and Unc-86.

Pit-1 is expressed during the development of anterior pituitary gland specially in the differentiation of somatotrophs, lactotrophs and thyrotrophs. The Oct-2 gene is B-cell specific gene that activates immunoglobulin genes. Oct-4 gene plays an important role in early cleavage. The Unc-86 gene is a nematode gene which is involved in the development of neuronal cells.

Lim Genes

Lim proteins constitute a large family of homeodomain proteins. These genes are involved in the formation of all parts of body. The development and maintenance of the head organizing center requires the expression of Lim-1 gene. Absence of Lim-1 protein results in headless embryo.

T-Box (TBX) Genes

These genes contain a T-box and also known as *Brachyury*. T-box genes encode a transcription factor that contain both repressor and activator domains. Now we know about a large number of T-box genes which are present throughout the human genome. These genes play important roles in development of mammary gland, upper limb and heart. Mutation of TBX-3 (present on chromosome 12) causes hypoplasia of mammary gland and abnormalities in upper limbs. Mutation in TBX-5 may cause atrial septal defects and absence of forearm.

Dlx Genes

The Dlx gene family consists of 6 members. Dlx genes operate in pairs and are closely associated with HOX genes i.e., Dlx-1 and Dlx-2 are associated with Hox d-13, Dlx-3 and Dlx-7 are associated with Hox b-13 and Dlx-5 and Dlx-6 are associated with Hox a-13. These genes play important roles in development of limbs, jaws and inner ear.

MOLECULAR CONTROL OF EARLY EMBRYONIC DEVELOPMENT

The following description is given so that students can get a glimpse of the utilization of molecules and molecular processes (as described above) in the development of embryo. Students will appreciate that each and every step of embryonic development is under the control of genes.

In the preceding part of this chapter we have seen that the development of human body is regulated by the cascades of gene expression. In this process genes are expressed in sequence, one after other, until the genes, which code for the actual structure and functional characteristics of cells or tissues are activated. As far as the early embryonic development is concerned, these cascades of gene expression are well studied in Drosophila, as compared to the vertebrates.

Our existing knowledge regarding the molecular basis for embryonic development is based mainly on studies on Drosophila (fruit fly). However, evidence is now available indicating that the basic body plan of mammalian embryo is under the control of many of the same genes that have been identified for controlling morphogenesis in Drosophila.

1. **How the axes of embryo are formed?**

The establishment of the axes is the first step in the development of embryo. The axes and early embryonic development in Drosophila is under tight genetic control but in human this part of development occurs under less rigid genetic control.

In Drosophila the development of anteroposterior, dorsoventral and right/left axes is under the control of a group of genes, which are called *"maternal effect genes"*. These genes are expressed out side the egg (within the mother fly) even before fertilization. For this purpose a large number of genes (*i.e., Bicoid, Swallo, Orkar, Torso, Cauda, Snake, Easter, pipe etc.*) express by coding transcription factors or growth factors. The products of these maternal genes are then carried into the egg where they establish gradients at the anterior and posterior poles of the egg. The gradients consist of RNAs and proteins that are differentially distributed in the common cytoplasm of the egg.

a. *Anteroposterior axis*

Three sets of genes determine the anteroposterior axis of the embryo.

- The *anterior end* of the embryo is determined by a set of *bicoid* genes. Bicoid mRNA is produced in the cells surrounding the oocyte and then exported to the anterior pole of oocyte. The bicoid protein is a transcription factor containing a helix-turn-helix motif for DNA binding. The mutations of bicoid genes produces embryo lacking head and thorax.
- The *posterior end* of a Drosophila embryo (abdominal segments) is determined by *nanos* class of genes.
- A third group of genes determines the most anterior (*acron*) and most posterior (*telson*) structures. The most important gene of this group is called *torso*. The gene torso codes for a trans-membrane receptor.

b. *The dorsoventral axis*

The dorsoventral axis of the embryo is determined by a separate set of genes. The Main gene for this axis is named *dorsal*. The product of gene dorsal forms the ventral to dorsal gradients in syncitial blastoderm.

In contrast to Dorsophila, where body exes are established even before fertilization, in mammalian embryos body axes do not become fixed until the end of cleavage or early gastrulation. The molecular control of formation of embryo (till the formation of bi-layer germ disc or before gastrulation) is not fully understood. The antero-posterior axis in human embryo is signaled by the cells of future anterior margin of the embryonic disc. This area of disc expresses the genes (*OTX2, LIM1, and HESX1*), which are necessary for formation of head. This is soon followed by the formation of primitive streak under the influence of *B-Catenin, BMP-4 and activin,* which are first expressed in the cranial region of embryo. Once the primitive streak is formed the embryonic axes (cranio-caudal, dorso-ventral and right/left) are well established.

2. Segmentation of embryo

The next step in the development of Drosophila is the division of embryo into identical segments. This is achieved by *"segmentation genes"*, which are subclass of genes called *"zygotic genes"*. The zygotic genes start expressing after superseding "maternal effect genes". The segmentation of oval shaped embryo of Drosophila is completed in three steps.

- The first step of segmentation is under the control of *"gap genes"* (*Hunchback, orthodenticle, tailless etc.),* which divide the embryo into broad regions.
- The second step is under the control of *"pair rule genes" (Hairy, runt, odd paired, odd skipped, paired* etc.), which subdivide the embryo in 7 segments along cranio-caudal axis (Fig. 12.8).
- The third step in segmentation is governed by *"segment polarity genes"* (*Gooseberry, hedgehog, patched, smoothened, wingless etc,),* which divide the embryo into 14 segments. Out of these 14 segments, the first three (C1-C3) differentiate into the head region; segments T1-T3 become thoracic segments, and A1-A8 give rise to abdominal segments.

At present similar segmentation genes are also identified in mammals. Now we know that segmentation of hindbrain, pharyngeal arches and somites are under the control of genes.

3. Determination of regional characteristics

Once the segmentation of embryo is completed, it is followed by imparting specific or regional characteristics to the newly formed segments of embryo. The regional morphogenetic characterization of individual segment of Drosophila embryo is brought about by the expression of a group of *"homeotic genes"*. These genes determine which embryonic segment should bear antennae, wings or legs. These 8 homeotic genes are

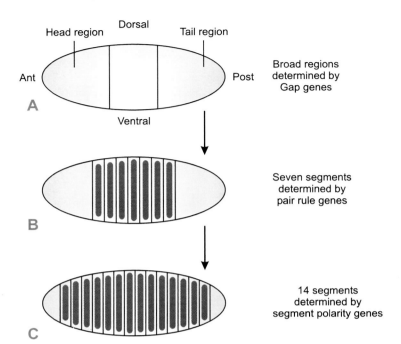

Fig. 12.8: *The process of establishment of the axes in a Drosophila embryo is governed by maternal effect genes. The segmentation of the embryo is controlled by segmentation genes (zygotic genes). Broad regions are determined by gap genes (A), seven segments by 'pair rule genes' (B) and (C) 14 segments by 'segment polarity genes'. (Courtesy of Prof. Inderbir Singh, Human Embryology, 8th edition, Macmillan.)*

situated on chromosome number 3 and are arranged in two groups (***Antennapedia*** and ***Bithorex)*** (Fig. 12.9) These genes are collectively called the ***homeotic complex*** or ***HOM-C.*** All 8 genes contain a highly conserved 180 base pair region of DNA called the ***homeobox.*** The homeobox encodes ***homeodomains*** of 60 aminoacids. This homeodomains recognizes and bind to specific DNA sequences of other gene.

The genes present in homeotic complex express themselves in a sequence i.e., genes, which are at 3' end of the DNA are expressed first and are for more cranial structures of embryo. While genes present at 5' end are expressed sequentially later and are for caudal structures.

The mutation of Antennapedia homeotic gene forms a leg instead of antennae. Similarly, mutation of ***Ultrabithorax gene*** causes third thoracic segment to develop as additional second segment, thus four wings are formed instead of normal two.

These homeotic genes of Drosophila are well ***conserved*** in humans and other mammals during evolution. The human genes (called ***HOX genes***) have same clustered organization, follow same order of arrangement within the cluster, their expression and functions are also the same as observed in Drosophila. The aminoacid sequences of homeodomains of Drosophila are upto 90% similar when compared with that of human. During hundreds

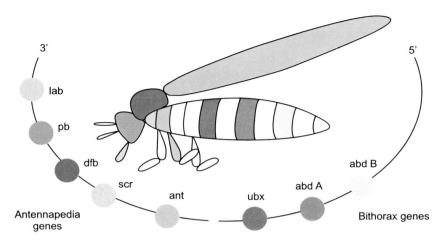

Genes are expressed in 3' to 5' sequence

Fig. 12.9: *Diagram showing the arrangement of homeobox genes of Drosophila on chromosome number 3. These eight genes are arranged in two clusters – Antennapedia and Bithorax. These genes are expressed in a cranio-caudal sequence. (Courtesy of Prof. Inderbir Singh, Human Embryology, 8th edition, Macmillan.)*

of millions of years of evolution these genes have duplicated twice so that humans have four copies of homeobox containing genes (***HOXA, HOXB, HOXC, and HOXD***) arranged on four different chromosomes (Chromosome number 7, 17, 12 and 2). Genes in each group are numbered 1 to 13 (Fig. 12.10). Genes with same number but present on different chromosomes form a ***paralogous group***. In all there are 39 genes and each gene contains Homeobox region, which encodes for homeodomain protein. Similar to fruit fly, homeobox genes of humans are also expressed sequentially in cranio-caudal direction during axis formation. The sequential expression of HOX genes correlates with the development of structures in cranio-caudal sequence.

The *HOX* genes are responsible for cranial to caudal patterning of the derivatives of ectoderm, mesoderm and endoderm germ layers. *HOX* genes regulate the differentiation of somites, vertebrae and hindbrain segmentation. The expression of individual *HOX* gene may occur in places like hair, blood cells and developing sperm cells. This indicates that though the main function of *HOX* genes is to set up structures along the main axis of the embryo, but the individual gene may also guide the formation of specific structure, which may not lie along the body axis.

Though there are 39 HOX genes in human but only two different kinds of malformations due to mutation in HOX A13 and HOX D13 are known. This may be due to the fact that the mutation of HOX might be lethal (embryo may not survive). Or it may be so that there is high degree of homology between HOX genes so that one HOX gene could compensate for the mutation in another. Mutation in HOX A13 is associated

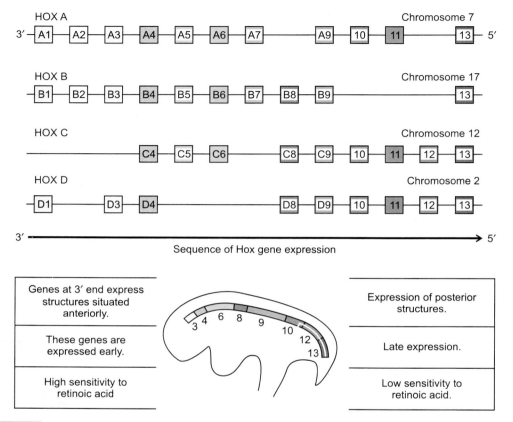

Fig. 12.10: *Alignment of four human HOX complexes. Expression of paralogous groups in the hindbrain and spinal cord, in cranial to caudal direction, are indicated by their numbers. (Courtesy of Prof. Inderbir Singh, Human Embryology, 8th edition, Macmillan.)*

with anomalies in limbs and genitalias i.e., shortening of first and fifth digits with hypospadias (or bicornuate uterus in females). Mutation of HOX D 13 gene results in synpolydactyly.

A number of other gene families also contain homeobox i.e., ***Paired:Pax (Pax-4 and Pax-6), POU, LIM etc,*** (Fig 12.7).

There is a direct relationship between vitamin A (***retinol***) and expression of *HOX* gene. Retinoic acid (metabolite of Vitamin A) plays an important role in the expression of HOX genes. Either too much or too little of retinoic acid causes misexpression of ***HOXB-1***. This may leads to abnormal development of legs, hindbrain and pharyngeal neural crest. The retinoic acid may cause extra pair of limb in frogs at the site of tail. This is an example of homeotic shift similar to formation of extra pair of wings in fruit fly. The genes which are closed to the 3′ end are more sensitive to retinoic acid than those at 5′ end.

13 Genetic Counselling

- Diagnosis of Genetic Disease
- Mode of Inheritance/ Risk of Occurrence
- Management of Genetic Disease
- Disputed Paternity
- Cousins Marriage
- Adoption

A t present there is very limited scope of treatment in genetics. Therefore the knowledge of human genetics can be used to avoid or reduce the incidence of some of the genetic diseases.

Whenever a patient suffering from genetic disorder or couples who are at risk, already having a defective child, consult a counselor, it is the duty of counselor to provide the following information.

DIAGNOSIS OF GENETIC DISEASE

It is important that the patient and his relatives should be informed about the correct diagnosis of the disease. They should also be informed about the prognosis and availability for treatment, if any. Reaching to a diagnosis may involve three steps:

- *Family history*
  One should make a detailed pedigree chart to analyse the mode of inheritance.
- *Examination of patient*
  A careful examination of patient will help to reach a correct diagnosis.

- *Laboratory investigations*

  This may include biochemical investigations, chromosomal analysis and molecular studies. In case of pregnancy, antinatal diagnostic aids e.g. amniocentesis etc. and imaging would be helpful to reach a correct diagnosis.

DETERMINATION OF MODE OF INHERITANCE/ASSESSMENT OF THE RISK OF OCCURENCE

Patient should also be told about the mode of inheritance of disorder i.e. autosomal/ X-linked/dominant/recessive. Couples having a defective child would like to know the chances of having normal or abnormal child from the next pregrency. This can be calculated on the basis of the knowledge of Mendelian inheritance. For example if the defect is autosomal recessive, and both the parents are carrier, there are 25% chances that the child may suffer from disease.

Once the numerical risk is calculated the patient and relatives should also be informed about the quality of risk in terms of high risk or low risk depending upon the type of disability produced by the disorder (e.g., high risk in case of mental retardation as compared to low risk in case of extra finger).

MANAGEMENT OF GENETIC DISEASE

Parents should be clearly told about the diagnosis and risk of recurrence involved. This will help parents to take their own decision. A counselor should also tell about all the options available for the management of disease. As for most of the genetic disorders treatment is not available hence, one should try to prevent the disorder.

- After prenatal diagnosis the couple should be told about risk of recurrence of genetic disease. However, the decision regarding termination of pregnancy has to be made by couple.
- If the couple is facing the problem of reproducing a normal child, they should be advised to think for adoption.
- If any of the parents is suffering from autosomal dominant disorder or if both mother and father are carriers of autosomal recessive traits then couple should be advised to go for artificial insemination by a healthy donor.
- The role of genetic counselor is just to provide all information regarding disorder including risks and options so that it becomes helpful to patients for taking their own decision.

GENETIC COUNSELLING IN DISPUTED PATERNITY

In case of disputed paternity, a genetic counselor may have to prove the paternity with certainty. Blood group matching between child, mother and putative father can only disprove paternity if the blood group of child does not match with both mother and putative father (i.e., if child is with blood group B, mother with A and putative father also with A).

Now the paternity can be determined, with certainty, with the help of **genetic fingerprinting** (see Chapter 15).

COUSINS MARRIAGE AND GENETIC COUNSELLING

There is always an increase risk of genetic diseases in offspring from the marriages between close relatives. The mode of inheritance of these diseases is usually autosomal recessive.

- If the offspring are from the mating between parent/child or brother/sister (first degree relative) then there are 50% chances that the offspring will suffer from the disease.
- Offspring from the marriage between uncle/nice or aunt/nephew (second degree relative) carry 5 to 10% risk to suffer from the disease.
- Similarly, offspring from the marriages between first cousins (Third degree relative) carries this risk between 3 to 5%.

ADOPTION AND GENETIC COUNSELLING

Sometimes couples may want to know the risk of developing a genetic disease by the child to whom they are intending to adopt. Risk can be calculated for the child of consanguineous or incestuous mating. However, it is difficult to determine the risk about adult genetic diseases which make their appearance in adulthood.

14 Prenatal Diagnosis and Treatment of Genetic Disease

- Indication for Prenatal Diagnosis
- Techniques for Prenatal Diagnosis
- Treatment of Genetic Diseases
- Gene Therapy

"Prenatal diagnosis" is the term used for the detection of abnormalities in a child (fetus) before birth. Prenatal diagnosis is utmost important for the couples who are at high risk of having a child with serious genetic disorder. This will help them to decide whether to continue with the pregnancy or not.

INDICATION FOR PRENATAL DIAGNOSIS

Which couples should be advised for prenatal diagnosis ?

- Couples having family history of genetic disorder or structural abnormality.
- As the advanced maternal age is associated with chromosomal abnormalities all pregnant women of 35 years or above.
- Family history of neural tube defect.
- Couples having previous child with a chromosomal abnormality, like Down syndrome.
- Woman suffering from insulin dependant diabetes or epilepsy.
- Mother as a carrier of X-linked recessive disorders.

TECHNIQUES FOR PRENATAL DIAGNOSIS

Following techniques are available for prenatal diagnosis.

- Amniocentesis
- Chorionic villus biopsy
- Fetoscopy
- Ultrasonography
- Maternal serum screening
- Fetal blood sampling

Amniocentesis

In this procedure the cells of a developing fetus are obtained for chromosomal analysis. The procedure is performed between 14-16 weeks of pregnancy. About 10 to 20 ml. of amniotic fluid is tapped through the abdominal wall avoiding injury to placenta. The amniotic fluid contains cells of foetal origin (from the amniotic membrane, fetal skin and urinary tract epithelium). These cells are used for obtaining of fetal karyotype (refer Ch. 3).

The amniotic fluid can also be used in the prenatal diagnosis of neural tube defects by estimation of **α-fetoprotein**. Its level is raised in amniotic fluid as a result of leakage from the open defects. The procedure of amniocentesis carries only 1% risk of abortion.

If the fetus is abnormal the termination of pregnancy in second trimester is advised. For the parents the decision, whether or not to abort a carrier or with a minor abnormality is always agonizing.

Chorionic Villus Sampling

In this procedure the chorionic villi sample is aspirated with the help of a catheter which is introduced through cervix. The entire procedure is carried out under the guidance of ultrasound. The chorionic villus sample is foetal tissue which contains large number of rapidly multiplying cells. Thus chromosome analysis becomes possible without cultivating these cells. As the procedure provides sufficient foetal tissue, biochemical assay or DNA analysis can also be carried out to detect single gene disorders.

This procedure is carried out during 10 to 11 weeks of gestation period (while amniocentesis is carried out during 14-16 weeks). Thus, if termination of pregnancy is needed it is safer and simpler in first trimester. With this procedure the risk of abortion is 2 to 3%. If the procedure is carried out before 9 weeks of gestation it may cause limb abnormalities in the embryo.

Fetoscopy

It is an endoscope for visualization of fetus. This fibro-optic self-illuminated instrument is inserted in the amniotic cavity under local anesthesia.

Indications for fetoscopy are as under

- Limb malformations
- Cleft lip, cleft palate, nose eye and ear malformations
- Malformations of genitals
- Skin disorders
- To obtain skin biopsy
- To obtain fetal blood sample from the umbilical cord.

With this procedure the risk of abortion is between 3 to 5%.

Ultrasonography

Ultrasound is a valuable instrument for prenatal diagnosis as it is safe for fetus and mother. These days it is routinely performed at 12 weeks of pregnancy.

Indications for ultrasonography are as under.

- Localization of placenta
- Diagnosis of multiple pregnancy.
- Diagnosis of malformations or structural abnormalities
- To ascertain fetal age

Recently, a correlation between chromosomal abnormalities and abnormal accumulation of fluid behind the baby's neck (**nuchal translucency, NT**) has been observed. Chromosomal abnormalities can also be indirectly detected by ultrasonography if fetus shows the **exomphalos** (umbilical hernia) and **rocker-bottom foot.**

Table 14.1 *Correlation between chromosomal abnormalities and congenital malformation detected by ultrasonography*

Congenital defect	Chromosomal abnormality
1. Exomphalos	Trisomy 13, 18
2. Rocker-bottom foot	Trisomy 18
3. Duodenal atrasia	Trisomy 21
4. Clenched overlapping fingers	Trisomy 18
5. Cardiac defects	Trisomy 13, 18 and 21
6. Nuchal Translucency (NT)	Down syndrome, turner syndrome, Trisomy 13 and 18

Maternal Serum Screening

The blood sample from the pregnant woman may be obtained at 16 weeks gestation to ascertain the presence of "**alpha-feto-protein**" (AFP). The raised level of AFP indicates the neural tube defects (anencephaly and spina bifida). The other conditions which are associated with raised AFP are:

- Multiple pregnancy
- Congenital nephrotic syndrome
- Abdominal wall defect
- Intrauterine fetal bleeding

The maternal serum screening is also helpful in prenatal diagnosis of Down syndrome. In the mothers of advanced age, the level of three biochemical markers is assessed. This is also known as "**triple test**". In this:

- Level of AFP is reduced
- Level of un-conjugate oestriol is reduced
- Level of HCG is increased

Fetal Blood Sampling

Fetal blood sample can be obtained with the help of ultrasound visualization. Blood is drawn from one of the vessels of the umbilical cord by putting a transabdominal percutaneous needle. The procedure is also known as "**cordocentesis**". The indication of the procedure is to make prenatal diagnosis of -

- Haemophilia
- Thalassaemia
- Sickle cell disease
- Immune deficiency disorders
- Chromosomal analysis

The procedure is also used in the management of rhesus isoimmunization. High risk of abortion (10%) is associated with the procedure.

TREATMENT OF GENETIC DISEASES

A. Prenatal treatment

At present, if the prenatal diagnosis of the genetic disease is made, it is difficult to provide the effective treatment in utero. In most of the cases parents have to opt for the termination of pregnancy. However, there is hope that prenatal treatment for few diseases may become available in near future.

At present disorders like **congenital adrenal hyperplasia** (CAH) and **sever combined immunodeficiency** can be treated in utero to some extent. In the earlier disorder low doses of dexamethasone are given throughout pregnancy while later disorder my be treated by giving transfusion of stem cells.

In utero fetal gene therapy

The cystic fibrosis has been treated successfully, in mouse, by in-utero gene therapy. Therefore hopes are there that it may become possible in near future to treat a genetic disease in-utero, in human, by gene therapy. It is hoped that the stem cell transplantation in-utero may treat many serious early onset genetic diseases.

B. Postnatal treatment

At present, the cure for most of the genetic disorder is not available. This is due to the fact that knowledge about the gene and gene products responsible for many diseases is still limited. For many disorders, even if we know the deficient gene product (enzyme, protein etc.) it is difficult to deliver them to target cells as proteins or enzymes are not normally transported into the cell. The correction of abnormal gene in somatic cells of tissues or organs, in which, the disorder manifest seems to be the possibility of distant future. However, many of the genetic diseases can be treated on the following lines.

Replacement of gene product

If the genetic disorder is due to deficiency or abnormality in gene product (enzyme or protein) then deficient or defective enzyme or protein can be replaced. The recombinant DNA technology has helped to synthesize the gene products in large quantities. Thus insulin is now being produced by incorporating human insulin gene in E. Coli. The other biosynthetic products such as growth hormone, factor VIII and IX, interferon, somatostatin and various vaccines are now being synthesized commercially.

Following is the list of some genetic disorders where replacement of gene product is used.

Disorder	Name of protein or enzyme to be replaced
Haemophilia A	Factor VIII
Haemophilia B	Factor IX
Congenital adrenal hypoplasia	Cartisone
Congenital hyperthyroidism	Thyroxine
Diabetes mellitus	Insulin
Short stature	Growth hormone

Drug treatment

In case of familial hypercholesterolaemia the drug **cholestyramine** helps to reduce cholesterol level. Similarly, in case of Wilson's disease penicillamine is used.

Tissue removal and tissue transplant

In case of hereditary spherocytosis (RBCs are spheroidal) splenectomy is carried out while for polyposis coli the colectomy is done.

Similarly, replacement of polycystic kidney by a normal kidney is the only available treatment for this genetic disorder. In case of diabetes cells of islet of pancreases from donor (after tissue typing and matching) are injected in the liver of the recipient. Thus patient can produce their own insulin.

Stem cell transplantation

The stem cell transplantation seems to be promising, in near future, in the treatment of genetic diseases. The patients suffering from genetic disorders like ADA deficiency, severe combined immunodeficiency, lysosomal storage diseases and Fanconi anemia can be treated by bone marrow transplantation. For this it is necessary that bone marrow tissue of donor should match with that of recipient. However, in case of stem cells derived from fetal umbilical cord may not have the problem of tissue compatibility.

If the genetic diseases like sever combined immunodeficiency, sickle cell anemia and thalassemia are diagnosed in utero the stem cells from bone marrow of donor can be successfully transplanted to the fetus without matching the donor and recipient's cells. There is no need to match these cells as fetal immune system is still immature and will not reject the donor's tissue.

Similarly the pluripotent embryonic stem cells can be transplanted in the specific tissues of the recipient. These stem cells differentiate as the healthy tissue of the recipient and remain functioning there for long time. In near future many diseases like Parkinson, Alzheimer disease, osteoporosis and myocardial infraction may be treated with the help of embryonic stem cells.

Dietary restriction

This is another important line of treatment of genetic disorders. Here patients of phenylketonuria are put on diet containing restricted amount of amino acid phenylalanine; galactose is restricted in galactosaemia and cholesterol in hypercholesterolaemia.

GENE THERAPY

Gene therapy is a new way to treat a disease. Replacing a defective gene with a normal gene to restore the lost gene function, in the patient's body, is the aim of gene therapy. The gene therapy is thus defined as the correction of an abnormal gene or replacement of defective gene by a normal functional gene.

The gene therapy is of two kinds i.e. **Germ line gene therapy** and **somatic cell gene therapy**. In the germ line gene therapy the genetic changes could be distributed to both somatic and germ cells and are therefore transmitted to future generations. At present, this kind of gene therapy is morally and ethically unacceptable universally. In somatic cell gene therapy the genetic changes are targeted to particular tissues or organs. This kind of therapy is universally acceptable.

Gene therapy involves the following steps:

- *Identification of defective gene*
- *Cloning of normal healthy gene*
  The cloning of DNA sequence involves not only structural gene but also the DNA sequences involved in the control and regulation of expression of that gene. The gene is generally cloned into a vector to be able to deposit the foreign gene into target cells.
- *Identification of target cell/tissue/organ*
  After identification of tissue, these cells are either isolated to treat in vitro and then genetically corrected tissue are returned to patient in a defective organ in vivo.
- *The method of insertion of a normal functional gene in the host DNA*
  Success of gene therapy lies in efficient gene transfer into the cell. Various methods have evolved in the past few years to transfer genes to the target cells.

  a. *Physical and chemical methods of gene transfer*
     - Microinjection of DNA into the cells
     - Electroporation (cell membrane is made more permeable by electric shocks).
     - Calcium-phosphate precipitation. In this method DNA is trapped in a fine precipitate which is endocytosed by the cell.
     - Cationic liposome mediated gene transfer - In this method DNA encapsulated in synthetic cationic lipid vesicles fuses with cell membrane and releases DNA into the cell.

  b. *Viral vector for gene transfer*

     Viral vectors are most efficient means of gene transfer. Some of the most commonly used viral vectors are adenoviruses and retroviruses.

     Adenoviruses are the common DNA viruses which do not integrate their DNA into host genome. Thus, disadvantage of this kind of vector is that the introduced gene is usually unstable.

     Retroviruses, which are RNA viruses, integrate their genome into the host DNA and use the cellular machinery to make its own viral proteins. Retroviral vector infect dividing cells and integrate therapeutic gene into target cells.

THE FIRST GENE THERAPY

The first gene therapy in human was carried out in 1990 by French Anderson on a child suffering from **ADA** deficiency. The ADA deficiency is a rare disease in which **adenosine deaminase** (ADA) is not synthesized. Due to this white blood cells become functionally inactive. As a result of these children with ADA deficiency essentially have no immune system (they are constantly sick as their bodies lack the power to fight microbes). Most of these children die before they are two years old (see also Ch. 10).

The gene therapy in case of ADA deficiency consisted of the following steps (Fig. 14.1).

- Blood was removed from patient.
- White blood cells were filtered out of the blood and red cells & fluid returned back to the body of patient.

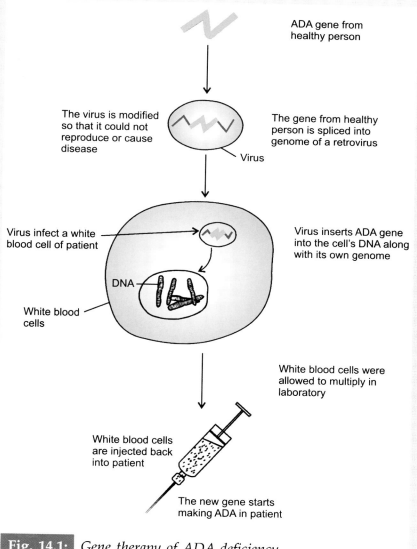

ADA gene from healthy person

The virus is modified so that it could not reproduce or cause disease

The gene from healthy person is spliced into genome of a retrovirus

Virus

Virus infect a white blood cell of patient

Virus inserts ADA gene into the cell's DNA along with its own genome

DNA

White blood cells

White blood cells were allowed to multiply in laboratory

White blood cells are injected back into patient

The new gene starts making ADA in patient

Fig. 14.1: *Gene therapy of ADA deficiency.*

- In laboratory, white blood cells were mixed with altered viruses containing ADA gene. These white cells were allowed to multiply for 10 days.
- These billions of white blood cells were then injected in patient. These white blood cells were carrying the life saving ADA gene.
- This treatment was repeated every month at first, but after few years it was found that one cell treatment a year was enough. (It should be noted that for long term treatment bone-marrow transplant is the only choice available at present.)
- This treatment improved the immune system of patient and patient started living the life of a normal child.

Today, more than 40 types of experimental gene therapy are in progress.

SUMMARY

- As there is very limited scope of treatment of genetic disease it is important to diagnose a genetic disease before birth so that parents can take a decision about continuation or termination of pregnancy. *"**Prenatal diagnosis**" is defined as detection of genetic abnormality before birth.*
- The prenatal diagnostic techniques are not used on a routine basis but is indicated for high risk pregnancies.
- Prenatal diagnostic techniques include **Amniocentesis; Ultra-sonography; Chorionic villus biopsy; Fetoscopy; Maternal serum screening and Fetal blood sampling**.
- Though treatment of many genetic diseases are not available at present but these can be managed to a certain extent by
  - Replacing the defective gene product,
  - Dietary restriction
  - Tissue removal and tissue transplant
  - Stem cell transplantation
  - Drug therapy
  - Gene therapy
- The gene therapy is a new way to treat a genetic disease in which an abnormal gene is either corrected or replaced by a normal gene.

15 Some Important Techniques in Genetics

- Recombinant DNA Technology
- DNA Cloning by PCR
- Nucleic Acid Probes
- DNA Sequencing
- DNA Fingerprint

- Human Cloning
- Human Genome Project
- Human Proteome Project
- Transgenic Animals
- Stem Cell Research

The aim of the present chapter is to introduce few important techniques used in genetics. This is intended to keep the students abreast of the progress in genetic technology. It is not essential for a medical student to know the details of these techniques. In this chapter only basic outline of these techniques are described and details are avoided.

RECOMBINANT DNA TECHNOLOGY

What is recombinant DNA technology or genetic engineering ?

One of the most important use of recombinant DNA technology is to clone a specific gene. The cloning is defined as making multiple identical copies, whether of genes, molecules, cells or whole organism. The specific gene for cloning may be obtained from genome; or by synthesis; or which is in the form of cDNA from mRNA. This technique is also used to clone the random DNA segments that are used as probes.

In a lay-man's term the recombinant DNA means formation of a new DNA fragment by combining DNA fragments from different sources. In this process of genetic engineering the DNA molecule is broken at two desired places to obtain a specific DNA segment or gene. This segment is then inserted into another DNA molecule at a desired position.

The DNA thus obtained is called recombinant DNA and the process is called genetic engineering. The recombinant DNA is then allowed to multiply in a host cell to obtain multiple copies of specific DNA segment or gene.

What is the use of genetic engineering?

Once the DNA fragments (genes) are obtained in large numbers after cloning, it can be used as follows:

- To find the gene structure
- For diagnosis of genetic disease
- Carrier detection
- Gene therapy
- Synthesis of hormones

How scientists got the idea of genetic engineering?

Most of the techniques of genetic engineering are based on our observations on the genetic behavior of bacteria and viruses.

Bacteria are single-celled organisms which multiply rapidly. A population of bacteria can multiply itself within few minutes. Hence, bacteria are commonly used by scientists to study genetics. The genetically engineered bacteria are also used in industries to make hormones, vaccine and enzymes. Bacteria and virus do not have cell nuclei and are called **prokaryotes**. All other living organisms have nuclei hence called **eukaryotes**. The DNA of bacteria is found on a single chromosome which is in the form of a large closed loop. In few bacteria DNA is also found in the form of few much smaller circles of DNA duplexes called **plasmids** (Fig. 15.1).

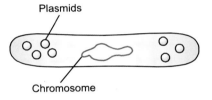

Fig. 15.1: *The DNA of bacteria is found in the form of closed loop chromosome and plasmids.*

Plasmids have the property that they can easily pass from one cell to another and can replicate at each cell division. Because of this property plasmids are used as vector (vide infra) in genetic engineering.

Virus contains the molecules of DNA or RNA within the protein coat. Though they contain genetic material but do not have the biochemical machinery needed for their own multiplication. Therefore to reproduce themselves, viruses take the help of bacteria. They settle on bacterial hosts and inject their DNA strand inside the bacterium. The DNA of virus uses the biochemical machinery of bacteria to form more DNA and more protein coats. Newly formed viruses rupture the bacterium and disperse into their surroundings. Scientists got the idea of genetic engineering from the behavior of viruses. They modified the DNA of virus (bacteriophage) which was then transmitted by virus to bacterial cells where it got multiplied.

Bacteria evolved defense mechanism against invasion of viruses. Since viruses attack by sending their DNA or RNA into the cell, bacteria counter attack by chopping up these foreign molecules into pieces with the help of their enzyme called restriction enzymes (because they help restricting the infection). These **restriction enzymes** are used as important tool by scientists in genetic engineering. These enzymes help to cut the DNA fragment at desired sites. Because in this technique (genetic engineering) a small fragment of DNA (gene) is needed to combine with other DNA fragment.

Thus the identification of plasmids , bacteriophages and **cosmids** (A cosmid is essentially a plasmid which has had all but the minimum vector DNA necessary for its multiplication) as vectors, and restriction enzymes (**restriction endonucleases**) helped scientists to evolve recombinant DNA technology.

Recombinant DNA Technique

This technique consists of obtaining desired fragment of DNA (gene) which is to be cloned; obtaining of a suitable vector; combining of DNA fragment with that of DNA of vector and transferring of recombinant vector to host organism.

Generation of DNA fragment:

For cloning of the desired segment of DNA we need to cut the DNA at specific sites. As stated above, this is achieved by restriction enzymes (restriction endonucleases). These enzymes recognize short sequences (4 to 8 base pair long) of double stranded DNA as target for cutting. There are about 300 enzymes now known which can recognize different specific sequences for cleavage. Restriction endonucleases are named on the basis of the organisms (bacteria) from which they are derived e.g. Eco RI is from E. Coli and Hind III is from Haemophilus Influenzae.

The restriction endonuclease always creates double stranded breaks. Since for each enzyme the cleavage site between two specific base pair is fixed, this may produce either a staggered or a blunt ended double helix DNA strand (Fig. 15.2). Thus, a desired DNA fragment is obtained by cut at two places in a DNA double helix.

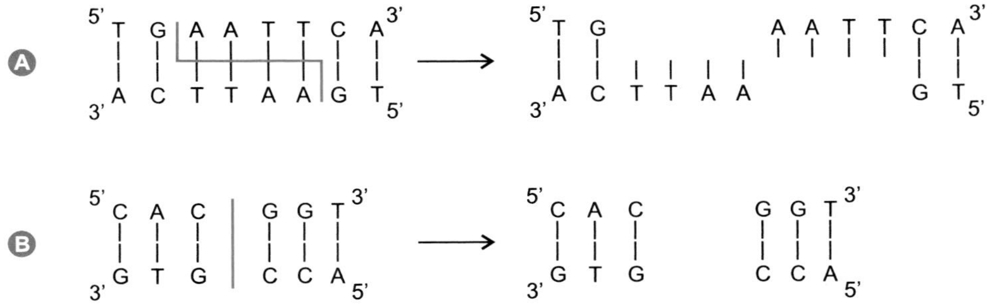

Fig. 15.2: *The staggered A and blunt ends B of double stranded DNA. In A the enzyme cleaved the strand between G and A bases and in B between C and G bases.*

Obtaining of vector:

The main aim of the recombinant DNA technology is to produce the clone of desired DNA fragment in large number. This can be achieved with the help of naturally occurring vectors. *A vector is a carrier of foreign DNA molecule which can replicate independently within a host organism to produce multiple copies of itself.* In this way the multiple copies of foreign DNA are also produced. Various types of vectors used for this purpose are plasmids, bacteriophages and cosmids.

Plasmids are the most commonly used vectors. As stated earlier plasmids occur naturally in bacteria and consist of circular duplex of DNA (Fig. 15.1). Plasmids possess limited number of sites where restriction enzymes can act. Another peculiarity of plasmid is that they carry genes for resistance to particular antibiotics. This fact can be used to identify recombinant clones.

Plasmids are obtained from bacteria after disruption and centrifugation. These are then cleaved by the use of restriction enzyme (Fig. 15.3).

Recombination of foreign DNA fragment with the DNA of vector:

When DNA has been cleaved by restriction enzyme which produces staggered ends, they are called "**sticky**" ends because they will unite with complimentary sequences produced by same enzyme on any other DNA molecule. As the same restriction enzyme is used to cleave the DNA fragment (which is to be cloned) and the DNA of plasmid, they will have identical complimentary ends (Fig.15.3). Thus the plasmid's DNA will combine with foreign DNA fragment. Their ends are sealed and stabilized with the help of another naturally occurring enzyme called **DNA ligase**. This enzyme is produced by cells to help the synthesis of DNA and repair of minor damage to molecule. The union of two DNA fragments thus produced is referred as **recombinant DNA molecule**.

Transfer of recombinant vector to host organism:

The recombinant DNA molecules are then introduced in host organism (bacterial cells). The cell membrane of bacteria is made permeable by exposure to certain salts or high voltage. Once the recombinant plasmids are taken up by host cells the plasmids will start multiplying. Thus the foreign DNA fragment will also duplicate along with plasmid's DNA each time the bacteria divide in two. In this way large number of identical copies (clones) of foreign DNA fragment (gene) will be obtained.

Screening of recombinant vectors:

When the recombinant vectors (plasmids) are introduced in host organism (bacteria) only few bacteria will take up these plasmids. Thus the culture media will be a mixture of bacteria with recombinant vectors and without recombinant vectors. Following facts about plasmids should be noted before understanding how to separate the bacteria containing recombinant vectors.

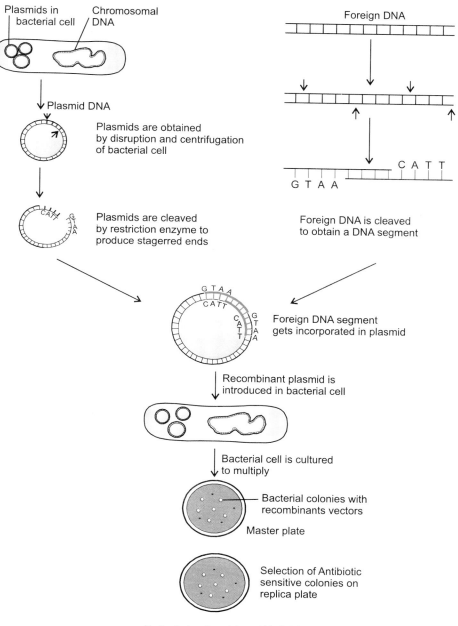

Plasmids in
bacterial cell

Chromosomal
DNA

Foreign DNA

Plasmid DNA

Plasmids are obtained
by disruption and centrifugation
of bacterial cell

Plasmids are cleaved
by restriction enzyme to
produce stagerred ends

C A T T

G T A A

Foreign DNA is cleaved
to obtain a DNA segment

Foreign DNA segment
gets incorporated in plasmid

Recombinant plasmid is
introduced in bacterial cell

Bacterial cell is cultured
to multiply

Bacterial colonies with
recombinants vectors

Master plate

Selection of Antibiotic
sensitive colonies on
replica plate

with the help of nucleic acid hybridization
(with radiolabelled DNA probe) and
autoradiography colonies containing
specific clone can be identified

Fig. 15.3: *Steps in recombinant DNA technique.*

Plasmids contain genes (segments of DNA) which are resistant to various kinds of antibiotics. These genes help bacterial host to save themselves from the action of antibiotics. Suppose if foreign DNA (gene) was introduced in plasmids by cutting its DNA strand at a site where there was the presence of gene resistant to ampicillin, then bacterial host cell will not be able to offer any resistance and will become sensitive to antibiotic ampicillin. However, the same plasmid will be able to resist tetracycline as the gene resistant to this antibiotic is intact.

For screening of recombinant vector the bacterial culture is taken to nutrient agar in a petridish and tested for their sensitivity to antibiotics on replica plating. Those colonies which are sensitive to antibiotic (as the gene is no longer functional) are identified as they contain recombinant clones. These colonies from master plate are picked and cultured separately. These cultures now will contain only bacteria (host cells) with recombinant vectors (plasmids).

Screening of clones with specific DNA sequence:

The "**nucleic acid hybridization**" method is used to screen the clones with specific DNA sequence (see later in this chapter). For this the colonies of host bacteria with recombinant clones are used. Once the clone with specific sequence is identified with the help of labelled probe (see later in this chapter) then the colony containing that clone can be identified on master plate and is cultured separately.

The recombinant DNA molecules generated as per the above technique can be collected and this collection is referred as a **DNA library**.

Applications of Recombinant DNA Technology in Humans

- Preparation of chromosome maps and analysis of DNA sequences.
- Production of drugs like insulin, somatostatin, blood clotting factors, growth harmone etc.
- Production of synthetic vaccines like anti-rabic, anti-malaria, anti-hepatitis, cholera etc.
- Biosynthesis of interferon from genetically engineered E. Coli. Interferons are first line of defense against viral infection.
- Production of monoclonal antibodies.
- Genetic engineering is useful in the diagnosis of genetic diseases.
- Gene therapy.

DNA CLONING BY PCR

In the above method of genetic engineering a specific DNA sequence was combined with the DNA of plasmid so that the foreign DNA can multiply with the culture of host bacteria. This kind of amplification of DNA sequence (gene) is known as **"in vivo" cell based cloning**. However, now gene or a specific DNA sequence can also be cloned with the help of **"in vitro" Polymerase Chain Reaction (PCR)**. A PCR machine can produce vast quantity of DNA fragment provided we know the base pair sequence of that DNA fragment. The machine needs very small quantity of sample (a single fragment of DNA or DNA of a single cell) and can produce a million identical fragments in only couple of hours.

Basic outline of PCR Technique

- For replication of DNA, in a living cell, a template DNA strand is needed against which polymerization of nucleotides can take place with the help of "**DNA polymerase enzyme**". This reaction also needs a "**primer strand**" to which further nucleotides can be added. If primer strand is not available the reaction can not proceed. However, in a PCR, primer strand is added from out side in the form of **deoxyoligonucleotide**. The DNA polymerase enzyme along with four essential nucleotide triphosphates is also added.

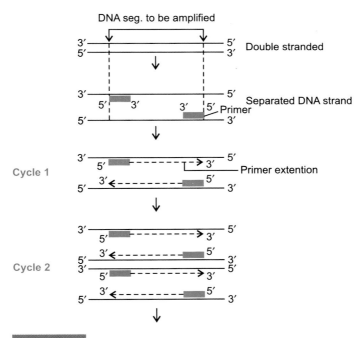

Fig. 15.4: *Polymerase chain reaction.*

- The mixture is incubated and this allows synthesis of complementary strand using primers with the help of polymerase enzyme.
- Previously, with each cycle of amplification of DNA in PCR, the temperature of mixture was alternatively increased (90 to 98°C) and decreased (40-60°C) for denaturation and renaturation of DNA. Denaturation was needed with each cycle to

separate the double stranded DNA. This was destroying enzyme polymerase and fresh supply of enzyme was added with each cycle. However, with the discovery of **"Taq polymerase"** enzyme, which acts best at high temperature (72°C), this problem of adding enzyme after each cycle of amplification was solved.

- The new automatic PCR thermal cycler can amplify DNA sequences at a fast speed. The PCR can clone DNA fragment within few hours while cell based in vivo DNA cloning techniques (genetic engineering) require days or weeks.
- New modified PCR are available which can produce mutation in DNA fragment as desired.

NUCLEIC ACID PROBES

Nucleic acid probes are single stranded small DNA or RNA segments of known sequences. These fragments are used to detect DNA or RNA fragments having same nucleotide sequences. DNA probes can be obtained from various sources like genomic DNA, cDNA or synthetic oligonucleotides. The probes are labelled either with radioactive isotopes or with nonradioactive signals molecules (biotin).

Some of the important uses of nucleic acid probes are as under:

- Probes help to recognize complementary sequences in DNA or RNA molecule. This helps to identify and isolate the specific DNA sequences from an organism.
- Probes are of help in diagnosis of infectious diseases.
- It is also used to identify the strain of an organism.
- Probes are used in forensic tests e.g. fingerprinting.

Nucleic acid hybridization

To Identify the specific DNA fragment (sequence) in genomic DNA following steps are involved before it is subjected to nucleic acid hybridization.

- DNA is extracted from tissue.
- DNA is digested with restriction enzyme so that it is cleaved into segments.
- The DNA segments of different sizes are separated by gel electrophoresis. The DNA fragments move on gel and their movement is inversely proportional to the size of fragments. The heavier fragments will remain closer to the site of loading while lighter fragments will move further away.
- Fragments of different sizes will appear as **bands** on the gel. These bands can be stained and visualized directly in the gel.
- These bands can also be isolated for further studies e.g. mapping of DNA sequences or to identify a particular gene (DNA segment) with the help of molecular probe.

To identify a particular band it has to be hybridized with a labelled molecular probe. To facilitate the hybridization, the band are transferred to nitro cellulose membrane by a technique called as **blotting**. Thus blotting is nothing but transfer of DNA, RNA or protein bands from gel to nitrocellulose membrane. Following are the various blotting techniques:

Southern blotting - This technique is used to blott DNA bands (Fig. 15.5).

Northern blotting - Here mRNA bands are transferred.

Western blotting - Here protein are transferred from gel to nitrocellulose membrane.

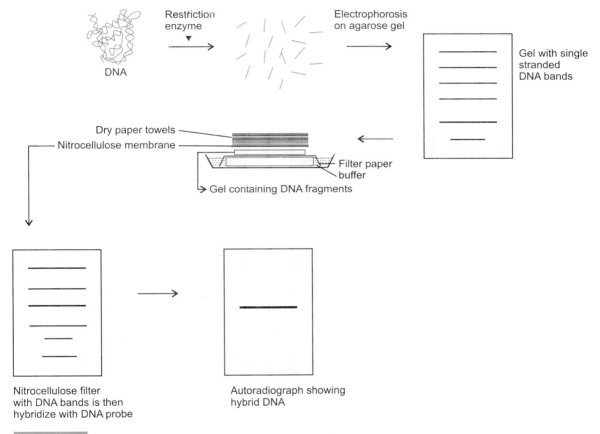

Fig. 15.5: *Southern blot technique for analysis of DNA segments.*

Southern blotting

In this technique the DNA sample is first digested with restriction enzyme which breaks the DNA in small fragments. This sample is then gel electrophoresed. The bands on the gel are then treated with alkali to make them single stranded (denatured). The gel containing DNA bands then placed on the top of a buffer saturated filter paper (Fig. 15.5). A sheet of nitrocellulose membrane is placed on the top of the gel. When buffer solution moves through gel (bands) to nitrocellulose membrane it carries single stranded DNA which binds on the nitrocellulose membrane. Thus DNA bands are transferred (blotted) from gel to membrane. Membrane now has the replica of DNA bands from gel. The DNA is fixed permanently on the membrane by heating at 80°C for 2-3 hours. This membrane is now hybridized with labelled DNA probe. The probe will form the complementary base pair with the homologous sequence on the DNA fragment. The nitrocellulose membrane is washed to remove any unbound DNA probe. This membrane is then exposed to X-ray film to get an autoradiograph of hybridized DNA.

DNA SEQUENCING OF GENE OR A DNA SEGMENT

After cloning or amplification of a gene or DNA segment by recombinant DNA technique or by PCR one can proceed for DNA sequencing. In this method nucleotide sequence of the given DNA fragment is determined. Following methods are used for DNA sequencing.

- Maxam and Gilbert's chemical degradation method.
- Dideoxy chain termination method.
- Automatic sequencing method.

The most commonly used technique is the dideoxy chain termination method. The automatic sequencer is the variant of this method.

Dideoxy chain termination method

In this method the single stranded DNA (whose sequence is to be determined) is used as template for DNA synthesis. This method is based on the principle that if during the process of synthesis dideoxynucleotides are incorporated then this will lead to termination of DNA synthesis. The termination of reaction is due to the fact that dideoxynucleotides lack a hydroxyl group at 3' carbon position which prevents its bond with next nucleotide.

- The single stranded DNA fragments (which is to be sequenced) are taken in four different reaction tubes.
- To all four tubes radioactively labeled four different deoxynucleotides; enzyme DNA polymerase I and oligonucleotide primers are added.
- To each tube one of the four dideoxynucleotides is added, so that each tube has a different dideoxynucleotide.
- The reaction will lead to synthesis of DNA fragments of different lengths.
- These fragments are then separated by electrophoresis, this is done for all four tubes on the adjoining lanes in the gel.
- The position of different bands in each lane is visualized with the help of autoradiography.
- From the position of these bands DNA sequence can be determined (Fig. 15.6).

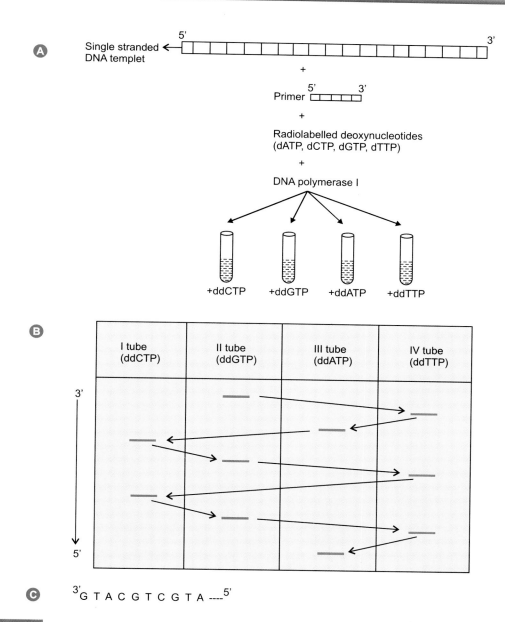

Fig. 15.6: *Dideoxy chain termination method of DNA sequencing. (A) Synthesis and termination of segments in reaction tube; (B) Electrophoresis and (C) Sequence determined by gel electrophorosis.*

Automatic Sequencers

This method is the further modification of dideoxy method. In this method different fluorescent dyes are attached to oligonucleotide primer in each of the four reaction tubes. The reaction mixtures are then electrophoresed in a single gel tube. A fluorescence detector measures the colour from gel tube and automatically records sequences. These computerized automatic sequencing machines are highly accurate and rapid. Only with the help of these machines it became possible to complete the human genome project much ahead of dead line.

DNA FINGERPRINT

The genome of each individual consists of series of non coding identical DNA sequences which are called repetitive DNA or tandemly repeated DNA sequences. These DNA sequences are highly polymorphic in nature and consist of 9-12 bp. However, they contain a common core which consists of 10-15 bp. The molecular probes containing the tandem repeat of this core sequences can identify the fragment of DNA which contain unique repetitive DNA. The pattern, length and number of these repeats are unique and specific for each individual. The above fact forms the basis of DNA fingerprinting.

DNA fingerprint is used in identification of an individual as it is unique for each individual (except for identical twins who would have same DNA fingerprints). This test is used to identify the suspected criminal and in case of disputed paternity.

Following are the steps of DNA fingerprinting:

- First step is to obtained DNA from blood, semen or from other cells of suspect (hair root etc.) This technique can also use the blood and semen stains and dead cells even if they are several year old.
- DNA is cleaved into smaller fragments with the help of endonucleases.
- DNA fragments are then separated by agarose gel electrophoresis.
- With the help of southern blotting technique these bands (fragments) are transferred to membrane.
- Radioactively labeled DNA probes are added on nitrocellulose membrane for hybridization.
- DNA probes binds the specific DNA sequences in the bands.

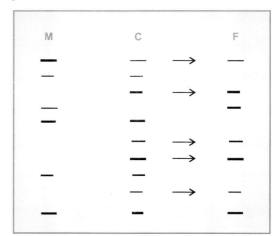

Fig. 15.7: *Finger-prints of mother (M), child (C) and alleged father (F). Arrows indicate bands common with father.*

- X-ray film is exposed to membrane to obtained the pattern of bands.
  This pattern of bands is known as DNA finger print

A certain identification of the suspect of the crime is made if all his fingerprint bands match with the fingerprints of the sample obtained from the crime scene.

For paternity determination DNA fingerprint of mother, child and alleged father are compared. If almost one half of the bands of child fingerprint matches with that of alleged father then paternity is confirmed (Fig. 15.7).

HUMAN CLONING

With the advancement of biotechnology and successful cloning of sheep "Dolly" by Dr. Ian Wilmut in 1996, the human cloning is now within the reach of scientists. However, the cloning of man is a matter of serious debate these days (should we or should we not go for human cloning?). All countries of the world have presently banned human cloning.

The cloning may be defined as technique by which *a large number of individuals can be generated which are identical in their genetic constitution (genotype)*. Thus the cloning is the production of a single or multiple copies of an individual.

The word "**clone**" means all the progeny from a single ancestor having identical genotype. In case of asexually reproducing organisms, like bacteria and amoeba, all the progeny carries the same genetic information as the original ancestor and are thus called **clonal descendants**. However, in higher organisms male and female parents are needed for reproduction. At the time of fertilization egg and sperm fuse with each other, each of which carries half the genetic information from each parent. Hence, the progeny can not have the identical genetic information (except in case of identical twins). This is the reason why the progeny of higher organisms are not clonal descendants or identical to each other.

For producing the clone of a higher animal it is necessary that genetic information should come from a single animal or parent whose clone is to be produced. All these information are stored in the nucleus of that individual. However, it is not possible to stimulate an adult somatic cell to develop like zygote. This is due to the fact that though all the genetic information are present in the nucleus of an adult somatic cell but it lakes the cytoplasmic control mechanism which an egg cell possesses. The cytoplasm of egg cell is responsible for initiation of zygote and embryo formation. The zygote cell has the capability to form a complete individual (it is said to be **totipotent**). With the subsequent cell divisions this capability (totipotency) is gradually lost. Now the embryonic cells differentiate to form different kinds of body tissues. Thus for the process of cloning it is necessary to make the differentiated adult somatic cells to lose their differentiated status and become totipotent like zygote cell. This is achieved by removing the haploid nucleus of egg cell (whose cytoplasm contains all the controlling mechanism for zygote formation) and replacing it by the diploid nucleus of a somatic cell from an individual whose clone is to be generated.

Steps in cloning:

- Many oocytes (eggs) are needed for the process of cloning as the rate of success of the procedure is too low. Therefore a female (who is going to donate eggs) is treated with hormones to stimulate the production of many eggs at a time.
- Another female, who will act as surrogate mother, is treated with hormones to make her uterus ready to receive the embryo.
- The nucleus from the eggs of donor mother is removed by microsurgery.
- The diploid nucleus from individual (who is to be cloned) is removed from somatic cells.
- One nucleus is microinjected in each enucleated egg cell (Fig. 15.8).
- This "**Chimeric cell**" (cell containing cytoplasm from one individual and nucleus from other) is cultured in laboratory till early embryonic development.
- This embryo is then implanted in the uterus of surrogate mother.
- The fetus thus produced will be a clone of nuclear-donor individual.

Advantages of human cloning:

- It is believed by some that cloning may help to improve the genetic makeup of human race.
- Many people may like to have their clones as it would preserve their all genes.
- Cloning may help infertile couples to have child of desired sex (female child if mother is cloned and male child if father is cloned).
- Cloning may be used as source of body parts for transplantation. As clones are genotypically same as recipient their body parts may not be rejected.
- Cloning has enormous economical potential by obtaining enzymes, hormones and various other pharmaceutical products by culturing the stem cells of cloned embryos.

Disadvantages of human cloning:

- At present no one is sure weather human clone will remain identical to donor as far as physical, behavioral and mental capabilities are concerned. This is because environment also plays an important role in the expression of genes.
- As far as improvement of genetic makeup of human race is concerned, the question will arise as to which race is genetically superior. This will further enhance the racial discrimination.
- Cloning will reduce the human diversity.
- It is expected that cloned individual may born with variety of developmental defects.
- To generate clones just for getting organs for transplantation is inhuman.

HUMAN GENOME PROJECT

The totality of DNA present in the cells of human is called human genome. The human genome contains billions of nucleotide base pairs in a set of 23 chromosomes. The field of genomics deals with the DNA sequence, organization, function and evolution of genome.

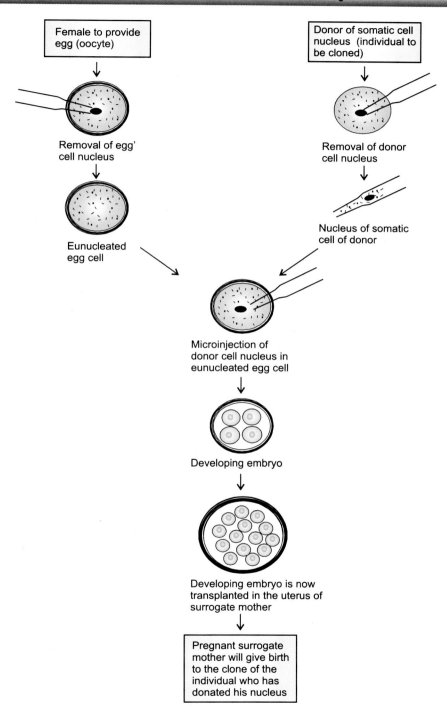

Fig. 15.8: *Basic steps in the production of cloned individual.*

The idea of **Human Genome Project (HGP)** came in the 80s with the object of sequencing all the DNA base pairs and to map the genes present in chromosomes. The HGP is a publicly funded international project of 15 years duration which started in 1991 in USA. This is the largest and most ambitious biology project ever taken. It involved 16 laboratories, 1,100 biologists, computer scientists and technicians of 6 countries (USA, UK, France, Japan and others). Though, previously it was thought to be a most difficult and time consuming task but with the invention of new techniques in DNA sequencing (auto sequencers etc.) the work could be completed before time.

The other group of scientists which also took the job of analysis of entire human gene sequence, is a private research organization **(Celera Genomic Corporation)**. On February 12, 2001 both the groups of scientists (HGP and Celera) simultaneously released the first detailed analysis of human gene sequence at press conference in London, Washigton DC, Brussels and Tokyo. These findings were published simultaneously in **"Science"** by Celera and in **"Nature"** by HGP.

Following are the objectives of Human Genome Project

- Sequencing of human genome
- Human gene maps
- Mapping of human inherited diseases
- Development of new DNA technologies
- Development of bioinformatics
- Functional genomics
- Comparative genomics.

Following are the highlights of the findings:

- There are approximately **3.2 billion bp** in human genome.
- There are about **26,000** to **35,000** genes in human being. This is in marked contrast to earlier estimate of 60,000 to 1,00,000 genes.
- Genes constitute less then 5% of human genome. Over 95% of the genome is called as **"Junk"** DNA (non coding DNA).
- The non coding DNA (junk DNA) contains segments of repeating DNA. These groups of **"repeats"** can be used as dating tools.. Based on such **"DNA dating"** scientists can build family trees of the repeats, showing exactly where they came from and when during evolutionary process.
- Hundreds of bacterial genes found their way directly into the human genome and not through evolution.
- Genes function as complex networks, rather then single entities producing specific proteins. The **"one gene-one function (enzyme)"** theory may now give way to a better genetic organization theory.
- The 99.9% of DNA is alike in all human races. Thus there is nothing like "superior race" and "inferior race".

The HGP has faced lot of criticism. However, the mapping of the location of genes on chromosome and the knowledge of sequences in a set of 23 chromosomes will help us by improving our understanding of various genetic diseases. This knowledge will ultimately be useful in prevention and treatment of these diseases.

THE HUMAN PROTEOME PROJECT

Proteomics is the study of all the proteins expressed by a genome. As stated earlier, in the human genome the number of genes are about 30,000 but the number of proteins expressed by these genes are more than 1,00,000 (which is due to events after transcription i.e., alternative splicing, refer Chapter 5). This clearly indicates that the study of proteins expressed by the normal and diseased cells or tissue is more direct and relevant method of understanding of diseases.

In this study proteins expressed by given tissue are separated by using two-dimensional gel electrophoresis. The pattern of the dots corresponds to the different proteins expressed on gel electrophoresis. By this method one can detect the expression of new protein in diseased condition. Non-expression, under expression and over expression can also be detected on two-dimensional electrophoresis image. By this technique one can also detect the post transcriptional modifications like change in the size and charge of protein on the proteome picture which is not possible by genome analysis.

TRANSGENIC ANIMALS

Mutated or manipulated genes can be produced in several copies (cloned). Such genes of interest can be injected into fertilized eggs of animals. These genes get integrated into the host chromosome and subsequently get phenotypically expressed. These genes are transmitted to the next generations as well. Such animals are known as knock out animals. Such models are used for studying various aspects of genetic diseases.

STEM CELL RSEARCH

Mesenchymal cells are harvested from adult bone marrow, neo-natal cord blood or donated IVF embryos and cultured. Specific differentiation is induced by providing required environment and growth factors. Differentiated cells are sorted out and characterized at each subsequent step for future culture. Cells are cultured till they differentiate further as per requirement. These cells are then injected at the site of damaged tissues for the purpose of regeneration and repair. Embryonic cells can also be used as models to study the effects of bacterial toxins, drugs etc. (See Chapter 14 also).

Index

NOTES

NOTES

NOTES

NOTES

NOTES